ScaleDown

WELLNESS WORKBOOK

NEW UPDATED EDITION

Danna Demetre

ENCOURAGING WOMEN TOWARD
LIFE-CHANGING FREEDOM

San Diego, California

ISBN 978-0-9883047-1-0

Unless otherwise indicated, Scripture is taken from the NEW AMERICAN STANDARD BIBLE®. Copyright © The Lockman Foundation 1960, 1962, 1963, 1968, 1971, 1972, 1973, 1975, 1977, 1995. Used by permission.

Scripture marked NIV is taken from the HOLY BIBLE, NEW INTERNATIONAL VERSION®. NIV®. Copyright © 1973, 1978, 1984 by International Bible Society. Used by permission of Zondervan. All rights reserved.

Scripture marked NKJV is taken from the New King James Version. Copyright © 1979, 1980, 1982 by Thomas Nelson, Inc. Used by permission. All rights reserved.

This publication is designed to provide accurate and authoritative information in regard to the subject matter covered. Whenever starting a new fitness or exercise program, Danna Demetre and Women of Purpose recommend a medical check-up first from a competent physician.

CONTENTS

INTRODUCTION

In This Section:

- Got a plan?
- Study Guide Schedule
- Helpful weight loss tools
- Partner up for greater success
- Getting started
- Personal Evaluations

Years ago, there was a television commercial about a delivery service that instructs a young male employee to transport a package as quickly as possible to "Fargo". He accepts the assignment with great enthusiasm and jumps into his car for a non-stop trip across the country reaching Fargo, North Dakota in record time. As he picks up the package to double check the address, he notices something very important. The package reads: John Fargo, Suite 300. Oops. The package was supposed to be delivered to a man named Fargo in the same building as the employee. It pays to pay attention to details.

Got a Plan?

It's really important to have the right information before starting on any journey. I believe the SCALE DOWN program and study guide will give you the best road map to reach your ultimate destination: A leaner, healthier body and a more balanced soul and spirit. This guide is designed as a companion to the SCALE DOWN book and the six-part CD or DVD program. You certainly can use the guide with the book alone, but you will have much greater success if you use all the tools available.

Watching or listening to the SCALE DOWN program more than once during the eight week journey will greatly enhance your ability to internalize and implement all that you are learning. You may choose to move at a faster or slower pace than I have designed; that's up to you. It is important to realize that you are not beginning an "eight-week program". Rather, this guide will help you begin living the principles necessary to achieve a truly sustainable and lasting lifestyle.

Study Guide Schedule

You will note that the study guide is formatted to watch or listen to one session each week from the The SCALE DOWN program in the first six weeks. The seventh week, you will dig a little deeper into the subject of calorie control, nutritious eating and sharing healthy recipes. Week eight is dedicated to the "Click Factor" – that is helping you discover your unique "motivating factors" and how to customize your self-talk to renew your mind in key areas.

Pace Yourself

Whether you are going through the program as a self-study or in a group, feel free to move ahead at your own pace. If you have the time, getting the whole picture in the first couple weeks and then going back through more slowly can be very helpful for those who want to get a jumpstart on their new lifestyle. Conversely, if the pace is too fast, simply slow down and process the information and assignments as you can. Too often, when people get overwhelmed, they simply quit or drop out. Don't do that! Commit yourself to the process and over time you will find small victories adding up to bigger victories that will reflect themselves in your body in tangible ways.

There are many aspects to this journey toward lifestyle victory that go far beyond simply changing your eating and exercise habits.

Remind yourself that this is a journey that will take time. Once you have the big picture, go back to your specific areas of weakness and concentrate on those. Just as we don't read the Bible once and put it down never to pick it up again, you will need to go back and reread and review some chapters.

The Power of Multiple Mediums

Research reveals that using multiple mediums (written, auditory and visual) can improve learning dramatically. SCALE DOWN DVD and CD programs will enhance your ability to learn and implement the principles taught in my book. If you are watching the DVDs in a group setting, I highly recommend getting your own copy of the program in CD form. Listen to them while exercising, driving or doing mundane tasks. The more often you input new information, the easier it will become to make it real in your own life. In addition, try to teach the most important principles you learn in each session to someone else. The act of teaching will help you internalize the concepts.

Helpful Weight Loss Tools

In the course of this program, you will read and hear me to refer to several weight loss tools that have been a great help to thousands of my clients over the last decade. Should you want to learn more about resources such as my biblically grounded Healthy Self Talk CD, simply go to the resource pages at the end of this guide or visit my website at www.dannademetre.com

Partner Up For Greater Success

There is no denying that teaming up with one or more people has tremendous benefit. Exchange phone numbers and email addresses and stay in touch once a week. You can even meet at the gym, take a walk together or enjoy a healthy lunch together. Pray for each other. Share your frustrations and successes. If you are not in a group program, I encourage you to find a friend who will join you and travel the lifestyle journey together. You could even begin a small group of your own.

Group Programs

If you do get your own group together, be sure and order a facilitator guide. It will give you helpful direction on how to lead a group effectively. It is recommended that you view one DVD per week in the first six weeks of your group program. Use the study guide to dig deeper into the subject covered, complete personal evaluations and design a lifestyle "recipe" in each key area. There are also key scripture and personal reflection or discussion questions at the end of each session. The studies can be done on your own or as part of a group, using the questions as topics for group discussion.

Weekly Format

There is a consistent study guide format each week which includes the following elements:

#1 Follow-Along Outline:

This section allows you to take notes and fill in some blanks as you watch or listen to the Scale Down...Live It Up programs in the first six weeks.

#2 Personal Reflection:

After each week's teaching, this section allows you to ask yourself some specific questions related to that week's topics. This can be done either individually or as part of a group discussion. Do be sure to jot down your initial thoughts and ideas and reflect on them later in the week.

#3 Build a Strong Foundation

This section digs into scripture related to the subjects. Again, you are asked to write your personal thoughts. If you are part of a group, this may be a good time to connect with a few others and share on a more personal level. If you are doing the program alone, this would be excellent for your devotions or quiet time once or twice during the week.

#4 Nourish Your Spirit

You will notice that each week, I encourage you to focus on four specific spiritual disciplines. Those are:

1. Pray as if it is the air you breathe.
2. Nourish your soul and spirit with God's Word daily.
3. Digest its truths through meditation.
4. Practice the presence of God.

You will also note that each week's emphasis in these areas differs depending upon the subject matter. So, don't assume that you've already covered these issues when you see the same headings each week. Take the time to dig deep, invest in your spiritual growth and surrender all your lifestyle challenges to God.

Obviously, this exercise needs to be done alone. Again, I recommend that you devote at least one day's devotion to this exercise. Then, try to bring these disciplines to mind all during your week as you go about your daily activities. So much of your long-term change will depend upon your commitment to "setting your mind on things above".

#5 Prayer for Each Week

Each week, I have written a prayer specific to that week's focus. I hope you will use it as an example of how you can be praying as you release all your struggles to God and seek His supernatural intervention in your life.

#6 Reading Assignments

Each week, you will also be encouraged to read the corresponding chapters in the SCALE DOWN book. If you have already read the book, I recommend at least skimming the chapters once again to reinforce those concepts that are not included in the DVDs or CDs. For those of you who are not "readers", please do read the entire book. There are many concepts and illustrations that simply could not be included in the Live It Up materials. You will miss some very important teaching if you choose not to read the book in its entirety.

Personal Evaluations

As with the Scale Down book, there are four personal evaluations within the workbook. Those key areas are: (1) Perspective/Motivation, (2) Burning Fat, (3) Nutrition and (4) Fitness. After taking the evaluation and computing your score, you find on the following pages a "menu" of healthy principles or actions and "recipe" page where you can choose the top three priorities you want to focus on in this area of your life. It is helpful if you transfer your "recipe" to an index card or into your day planner if you use one. That way you can refer to it occasionally during the week and remind yourself of your plan.

I also recommend re-taking the evaluations periodically as you progress in your lifestyle journey. Use a different colored pen each time. Take some time to review these evaluations and put your greatest attention in the area of your greatest weakness.

As you progress through each of the weekly assignments, please realize that you don't need to complete every single assignment. You may be strong in an area that you can simply skip. On the other hand, there may be areas that you will need more time. The eight-week guide is simply a suggested way to systematically ingest and begin to apply many mental, physical and spiritual principals to your life.

Initial Evaluation – Gaining Perspective

You are about to embark on a journey with Scale Down. The following questions will help you understand your personal desires and level of commitment from the outset.

1. What physical, mental, emotional and spiritual changes do you hope to achieve?

2. Why is this important to you?

3. For whom do you want to make these changes or improvements?

4. How do you think they will change your life?

5. What will it cost you (in time, energy, money, etc.)?

6. Are you willing to pay that price?

7. Do you believe you can do this with God's help?

Okay, now it's time to get started with the program. I recommend that you spend a few minutes every day reading your book and reflecting on the key spiritual perspectives in that section. It's been said that "We make time for that which is most important to us." If this is true and your body and health are important to you…please make the time. It will be well worth it.

WEEK 1

The Body Battle

In This Section:

- The 3 Keys to Permanent Weight Loss
- 7 Small Steps to Permanent Change

Follow-Along Outline:

View or listen to session one as you complete the blanks in this outline and jot down your own notes or thoughts in the margins. Then, complete the study guide assignments for this week at the end of this section individually or with your group.

Knowing what to do is easy. Getting yourself to do it...Now that's the challenge!

Scale Down Overview

- Understanding the balance of body, soul and spirit.
- Realizing that "you are what you think."
- Discovering the power of your true identity.
- Accessing the weapons to fight the "battle of the flesh".
- Eating for high energy and health.
- Burning fat to the max!

The Three Keys To Permanent Weight Loss

Balancing body, soul & spirit

The Lies
- A supplement or pill will solve your problems.
- You must "diet" to lose weight.
- You can lose a pound a day!

The Truth
- There are no quick fixes or magic bullets...it's up to

  _____!

- It takes more time to _____weight than _____

  weight.

- You have to lose weight the _____ way you plan to

  keep it off.

To lose weight permanently, you have to take it off the same way you plan to keep it off. The only realistic way is through a lifestyle change. Ask yourself this question: "Can I eat and exercise this way most days for _____

_____?"

If the answer is no, you've just gone on another diet!

Key #1: THE BODY

"Present your bodies as a living and holy sacrifice, acceptable to God, which is your spiritual act of worship."

—Romans 12:1

1. The bottom line to losing excess fat is simply:

   _____ in versus _____ out!

2. FACT: The average person gains 25 pounds between the ages of 30 and 50 years old. Question: How many extra calories must be consumed each day for this to happen?

   A. 5 to 10   B. 50 to 100   C. 250 to 300

3. The average American woman burns _____ calories per day:

   A. 1,000 – 1,200   B. 1,300 – 1,500 C. 1,600 – 1,700

4. If I burn 100 calories more each day than I eat, it will take me _____ days to burn off one pound of fat.

The "100" Calorie Rule:

For every 100 calories "extra" you burn each day, you will lose about ten pounds of fat off your body each YEAR.

The "500" Calorie Rule:

For every 500 calories "extra" you burn each day, you will lose about one pound of fat off your body each WEEK or 52 pounds each YEAR.

We build a completely new body every _____ years.

Therefore, I must remember each and every day that I _____ what I _____!

Key #2: THE SOUL

"Do not be conformed to this world, but be transformed by the renewing of your mind..." —Romans 12:2

1. Your mind is the _____ of your

    _____.

2. To change your habits or behavior, you must first change your

    _____.

3. In the human brain, the most

    _____ thought wins.

4. To change your mind, you must _____ and

    _____ old negative programs.

5. Before you can change unhealthy thinking, you must
    identify the _____ you believe and replace them with

    _____.

Get a New Attitude:

- The "All Or Nothing" Attitude
- The "Quit Before You Start" Attitude
- The "I Don't Have Time" Attitude
- Get a _____Attitude!

Key #3: THE SPIRIT

"Whether then, you eat or drink or whatever you do, do all to the glory of God."

—1 Corinthians 10:31

1. _____ your goals and desires for your body, mind and spirit to God.

2. He who walks by the Spirit will not fulfill the desires of the _____.

3. Pray for enough _____ for the moment.

4. Ask yourself this question: Does this attitude, behavior, eating plan or lifestyle _____ God?

5. _____ as if it's the air you breathe.

6. _____ your spirit with God's Word daily.

"God will not give us good habits; He will not give us character; He will not make us walk aright. Wes have to do that for ourselves. Beware of the tendency of asking the way when you know it perfectly well." ~Oswald Chambers

7 Small Steps Toward Permanent Change

1. Evaluate your lifestyle in four key areas:

   (1) _____

   (2) _____

   (3) _____

   (4) _____

2. Grow in knowledge about _____ and

   _____.

3. Find ways to eat fewer _____ each day.

4. Burn more calories by moving

   _____ each day.

5. Measure your success by changes in your attitude and behavior,

   not the _____.

6. Renew your mind with _____.

7. Do the right things for the right reasons… and

   _____ the results!

Small steps, taken consistently, add up in

a BIG way over time!

Review these checkpoints toward a victorious lifestyle daily:

Consider putting these checkpoints on an index card or somewhere in your daily planner where you can review them daily to remind you of the healthy, positive perspectives that will help you reach your long-term lifestyle goals.

- ☐ I am finding creative ways to eat fewer calories every day.
- ☐ I am finding simple ways to burn more calories every day.
- ☐ I am learning to eat for maximum energy and health.
- ☐ I am making purposeful activity or exercise a regular habit.
- ☐ I am identifying and changing my unhealthy beliefs and attitudes.
- ☐ I am building a foundation of truth from God's Word to live victoriously.
- ☐ I am becoming transformed by the renewing of my mind.
- ☐ I am learning to see myself and my goals through God's eyes.

PERSONAL REFLECTION

Answer the following questions on your own or with your group:

1. Identify the most damaging "lie" you believe that is sabotaging your lifestyle success and write it here:

2. What new attitude is the single most important one to work on during your Scale Down journey? Write it here:

3. Decide on three ways to eat fewer calories this week and write them below:

(1) _____

(2) _____

(3) _____

4. Determine three ways to burn more calories this week and write them below:

(1) _____

(2) _____

(3) _____

BUILD A STRONG SPIRITUAL FOUNDATION

Meditate on this scripture and answer the corresponding questions:

"Present your bodies as living sacrifices, holy and pleasing to God, this is your spiritual act of worship."

—Romans 12:1

1. Why is it so difficult to present our bodies as living sacrifices?

2. How can you begin to truly see your body as a means of worshiping God?

3. Do you think this awareness will help you in changing your lifestyle?

NOURISH YOUR SPIRIT

Spiritual life-changing victory requires daily nourishment. Nourish your spirit daily in four ways:

1. Pray as if it is the air you breathe.

Pray the prayer below this week, surrendering every dimension of your life to the Lord. Add your own thoughts and words each day and give God your entire life – body, soul & spirit.

2. Nourish your soul and spirit with God's Word daily.

Read and reread Romans 12:1 and ask God to show you how this scripture relates to you personally.

3. Digest its truths through meditation.

Imagine God's pleasure as you present your body as a living sacrifice. See Him delighting as you make sacrifices in your lifestyle because you know He is pleased when you take good care of yourself and invest in your long-term health and energy.

4. Practice the presence of God.

Remind yourself throughout the day that God is constantly with you and cares about all the details of your life. He loves you just the way you are, but truly wants the very best for you as you walk and live in this physical world.

PRAYER FOR WEEK ONE

Lord, I commit this journey to You. I pray that you will be glorified as I seek wisdom and strength to do the "right things for the right reasons". Thank you for the incredible body you have given me. I present it as a living sacrifice. Please help me to glorify you in it as I move out of bondage to my unhealthy thinking and habits. Show me where I'm believing lies. Help me to replace those lies with truth. In Jesus' name, Amen.

SUGGESTED READING – WEEK ONE

Read the following chapters in *Scale Down* and check off below:

Chapter 1: The Battle of the Body
- "I hate my body! What about you?"
- Danna's personal story

Chapter 2: Getting Started
- It's just four short pages... You can do it!

Chapter 3: Evaluate Your Lifestyle
- Evaluation #1: Perspective/Motivation
- Evaluation #2: Fat Management
- Evaluation #3: Nutrition
- Evaluation #4: Fitness

Chapter 4: Sweat the Small Stuff
- The bottom line to YOUR bottom line
- Common weight loss lies
- The ABCs of lifestyle change
- Get a new attitude!

WEEK 2

Beneath the Surface

In This Section:

- Balancing Body, Soul and Spirit
- Discovering Your True Identity
- Building a Healthy Body Image

Follow-Along Outline:

View or listen to session two as you complete the blanks in this outline and jot down your own notes or thoughts in the margins. Then, complete the study guide assignments for this week at the end of this section individually or with your group.

Beneath the Surface

Balancing Body, Soul & Spirit

"For this reason, I say to you, do not be worried about your life, as to what you will eat or what you will drink; nor for your body, as to what you will put on. Is not life more than food and the body more than clothing?" —Matthew 6:25

The overextended life

What are my excuses?

Juggling the balls of life

The Rubber Balls

The Glass Balls

The Expanding Balloon

BALANCE — What it is NOT

- ☐ It is NOT an expertly managed lifestyle
- ☐ It is NOT reaching all your goals and in record time
- ☐ It is NOT success
- ☐ It is NOT a stress-free life

BALANCE — What it IS

- ☐ It IS living with a godly perspective
- ☐ It is making choices based on truth
- ☐ It is doing the "right things" for the "right reasons"
- ☐ It is leaving the results up to God

The "ONE THING"

- ☐ Physical _____
- ☐ Material _____
- ☐ Mental _____

- ☐ Emotional _____
- ☐ Relational _____
- ☐ Spiritual _____

The Ultimate "ONE THING"

- ☐ Pray as if it is the air you breathe.
- ☐ Nourish your soul and spirit with God's Word daily.
- ☐ Digest its truths through meditation.
- ☐ Practice the presence of God.
- ☐ Worship Him in Spirit and in truth.

Questions to help balance your life:

- ☐ What is the worst thing that can happen if I don't say "yes" to this activity or opportunity or don't get this "thing" accomplished?

- ☐ Will it help me know and love God more?

- ☐ Will it help me know or love my family more?

- ☐ Will this help me love others more?

- ☐ Why else am I choosing this?

Beneath the Surface

Discovering Your True Identity

Therefore if anyone is in Christ, he is a new creature; the old things have passed away; behold, new things have come.
—2 Corinthians 5:17

Who Are You?

What three words best describe you?

1. _____

2. _____

3. _____

What is your most important role?

Who is most important in your life?

You are NOT:

☐ Your roles
☐ Your relationships
☐ Your behavior

What's Love Got To Do With It?

- ☐ Love is an incredible motivator.
- ☐ Pure love empowers us to obey and glorify God.
- ☐ It gives us a sense of significance, value and purpose.
- ☐ It becomes a driving force and motivation behind all we desire.

Beneath the Surface

Building a Healthy Body Image

"For man looks at the outward appearance, but the Lord looks at the heart." —1 Samuel 16:7

What is a "healthy" body image?

TRUE OR FALSE? Answer the following questions to discover how you view yourself physically.

- _____ I dislike my overall physical appearance.
- _____ I'm unhappy with the size and shape of my body.
- _____ I am ashamed to be seen in a swimsuit.
- _____ I feel other people must think that my body is unattractive.
- _____ I compare myself to others.
- _____ I am self-conscious about my appearance.
- _____ My body preoccupies my thinking many times during the day.

Three things I LIKE about my physical body:

1. _____

2. _____

3. _____

Three (non-physical) things I LIKE about myself:

1. _____

2. _____

3. _____

Three things I do NOT LIKE about myself:

1. _____

2. _____

3. _____

> *"I will give thanks to You, for I am fearfully and wonderfully made; wonderful are your works, and my soul knows it very well." —Psalm 139:14*

Tell yourself the truth:

- ☐ "With God's help, I can change my body and accept myself."
- ☐ "I celebrate who I am."
- ☐ "I am more than just a physical body."
- ☐ "I see myself as a wonderful creation of God."
- ☐ "I can enjoy life without always thinking about how I look."
- ☐ "I am focusing on my strengths more than my perceived flaws."

PERSONAL REFLECTION:

Answer the following questions on your own or with your group:

1. Where is your life most out of balance? What can you begin doing right now to change that?

2. What "one thing" would make the biggest difference in your physical dimension and how can you begin to address that daily?

3. What "one thing" would make the biggest difference in your spiritual dimension and how can you begin to address that daily?

4. How is your body image affecting your life and how will you change that?

BUILD A STRONG SPIRITUAL FOUNDATION

Meditate on the following scriptures and answer the corresponding questions:

> *"For this reason, I say to you, do not be worried about your life, as to what you will eat or what you will drink; nor for your body, as to what you will put on. Is not life more than food and the body more than clothing?"* —Matthew 6:25

1. Is stress and worry impacting your life and/or lifestyle?

2. How can trusting the Lord for the details of life help you live a healthier lifestyle?

*"Delight yourself in the Lord and He will give you
the desires of your heart." —Psalm 37:4*

1. How does delighting in the Lord impact the desires of our heart?

2. How will your desires influence your motives and/or your behavior?

NOURISH YOUR SPIRIT

Spiritual life-changing victory requires daily nourishment. Continue to nourish your spirit daily in four ways:

1. Pray as if it is the air you breathe.

Pray the prayer below each day this week, surrendering every dimension of your life to the Lord.

2. Nourish your soul and spirit with God's Word daily.

Read or memorize the two scriptures above (Matthew 6:25 and Psalm 37:4) and repeat them at least twice each day.

3. Digest its truths through meditation.

Meditate on what it means to "delight in the Lord". Imagine what your life would be like if your "one thing" was to delight in Him.

4. Practice the presence of God.

Imagine eating every meal and spending every second of each day in His presence. The truth is...you ARE!

PRAYER FOR WEEK TWO

Heavenly Father, I am so thankful that I am a new creation in Christ. Thank you for making all things new. Please help me to not only know this truth, but to believe it deep within my soul. I pray that you will also help me to identify the areas of my life that are out of balance and to surrender those areas to You. Help me learn to choose the "best" from all the "good" and to have realistic expectations about life. Lord, I celebrate that I am "fearfully and wonderfully made". I pray you will help me see my physical body from your perspective and stop comparing myself to others or to society's standard of beauty. Please remind me in my insecurity that I am the apple of your eye and beautiful inside and out. Amen.

SUGGESTED READING – WEEK 2

Read the following chapters in *Scale Down* and check off below:

☐ *Chapter 5: Balancing Body, Soul and Spirit*
- Finding balance in your life
- What would you do if your steering wheel came off while you were driving down the freeway??? Read Danna's story in this chapter!

☐ *Chapter 6: Discovering Your True Identity*
- Who are you?
- What's love got to do with it?
- Surviving an affair

☐ *Chapter 7: Building a Healthy Body Image*
- Accepting our flaws
- God's perspective on beauty and our body

WEEK 3

You Are What You Think

In This Section:

- Renewed Mind...Transformed Body
- The Battle of the Flesh
- Lifestyle Evaluation and Plan for Healthy Thinking

Follow-Along Outline:

View or listen to session three as you complete the blanks in this outline and jot down your own notes or thoughts in the margins. Then, complete the study guide assignments for this week at the end of this section individually or with your group.

You Are What You Think

Renewed Mind...Transformed Body

"Do not be conformed to this world, but be transformed by the renewing of your mind." —Romans 12:2

Your Mind...The Ultimate Computer

- ☐ The freeways of the mind
- ☐ Automatic Pilot
- ☐ Garbage in... garbage out!
- ☐ Good stuff in... good stuff out!
- ☐ We are "leaky buckets"
- ☐ Erasing old tapes
- ☐ Building New Pathways

God's Prescription for a Healthy Mind

#1 Pure Thinking

"Whatever is true, whatever is noble, whatever is right, whatever is pure, whatever is lovely, whatever is admirable, if anything is excellent or praiseworthy, think about such things."
—Philippians 4:8

#2 Positive Modeling

"Whatever you have learned or received or heard from me or seen in me; put into practice and the God of peace will be with you." *—Philippians 4:9*

#3 Practiced Obedience

- ☐ Observation
- ☐ Imitation
- ☐ Repetition

The Power of Self-Talk

Old negative message:

"I blew it again. I'll never lose weight!"

New healthy message:

"I CAN lose weight one small step at a time!"

Old negative message:

"I always end up quitting and never reach my goals."

New healthy message:

"I'm not quitting. With God's help, I can reach my goals."

Old negative message:

"I'm addicted to chocolate."

New healthy message:

"I'm in control of every bite that goes in my mouth."

Old negative message:

"I hate to exercise; and besides, I don't have time."

New healthy message:

"I make time to exercise and I love it!"

The power of God's word

"The Word of God is living and active and sharper than any two-edged sword, and piercing as far a s the division of soul and spirit, of both joints and marrow, and able to judge the thoughts and intentions of the heart." —Hebrews 4:12

Your Healthy Thinking Tools

- ☐ Attitudes
- ☐ Self Talk
- ☐ People Power
- ☐ Goals
- ☐ Journaling
- ☐ Logging

Watch your thoughts; they become your words.

Watch your words; they become your actions

Watch your actions; they become your habits.

Watch your habits; they become your character.

Watch your character; it becomes your destiny.

The Battle of the Flesh

"For what I am doing, I do not understand;
for I am not practicing what I would like to do,
but I am doing the very thing I hate." —Romans 7:15

Choosing Your Path

- ☐ The path of least resistance
- ☐ The path of self-discipline
- ☐ The zig-zag path
- ☐ The path with real power

But I say, walk by the Spirit, and you will not carry out the desire of the flesh." —Galatians 5:16

God's Part

- • _____

- • _____

- • _____

Your Part
- ☐ Draw near to God
- ☐ Abide – Settle down and be at home
- ☐ Resist the devil
- ☐ Study and meditate on the Word
- ☐ Prayer
- ☐ Praise
- ☐ Thanksgiving

"But the fruit of the Spirit is love, joy, peace, patience, kindness, goodness, faithfulness, gentleness and self-control; against such things there is no law." —Galatians 5:22-23

Are You...Addicted To God?

1. Set your _____ on things above.

2. _____ in the Vine.

3. Walk in the _____.

4. Become "_____" to God.

5. Surrender your _____ to the Lord.

6. _____ each meal is taken with Jesus.

7. Pray for enough grace for the _____.

Evaluate Your Lifestyle

Perspective/Healthy Thinking
A personal lifestyle evaluation

Objective: Identify your lifestyle speed bumps

Action: Take the lifestyle self-evaluations

Starting a new program without a good evaluation is like letting the dentist drill on your teeth before he takes x-rays!

Truth

Ignorance is not bliss! If you don't know what the problem is, it's hard to fix it. So it's time to be totally honest with yourself. Excuses and rationalizations undermine your achievement. Only the truth will set you free. An ancient philosopher said, "Know thyself". It wasn't bad advice.

We will begin by taking the Perspective/Healthy Thinking self-evaluation. This will give you a good snapshot of your current strengths and weaknesses in the area of your thinking—very important! If you don't clearly understand your weaknesses, it's hard to set priorities and take action.

How to take the evaluation

Spend about four to five minutes on the evaluation. Base your answers on your most consistent behavior or attitudes in the past three months.

- DON'T rate yourself based on any changes you've made in the last 4 to 6 weeks.
- DO rate yourself based on your first impression and move on.
- DON'T go back and "readjust" your answers if you don't like the score!
- DO remember... this is a reality check. Just face the truth and move on.

Now, it's time to face the music. Grab a pencil and be completely honest. No one has to see the results but you!

Lifestyle Evaluation:
Perspective/Healthy Thinking

Based on the last three months, please rate yourself as:
0 = Almost Never   1 = Sometimes   2 = Often   3 = Always

_____ I see myself as a fully accepted and loved child of God.

_____ My choices and actions are made based on my relationship to Christ.

_____ I am thankful for the body God has given me.

_____ I honor God with my lifestyle habits.

_____ I take responsibility for my body's size, shape and health.

_____ My attitude is this: I am not my behavior. I am complete in Christ.

_____ I surrender my weaknesses to God and rely on His strength for the moment.

_____ My personal goals are realistic and honor God.

_____ I take realistic steps toward my goals each day.

_____ I know that with God's help, I can have a lean, healthy body.

_____ I am aware of the lies I believe about my body, looks and health.

_____ I recognize and choose not to accept this negative thinking.

_____ I renew my mind with God's truth each day.

_____ I am a work in progress and God delights in each good step I take.

_____ Each day, I choose to submit my body, mind and spirit to God.

_____ I pray daily for God's strength to walk in the Spirit and not fulfill the desires of my flesh.

_____ *Add the total of all scores*

How did you do?

Your success depends upon your ability to prioritize your goals, design a realistic plan and surrender it daily to God.

Design a HEALTHY THINKING Success Recipe

You've evaluated your thinking. You've educated your mind. Now it's time to initiate a new plan. It's unrealistic to make too many changes all at once. You'll just burn out and give up. Your success depends upon your ability to prioritize your goals and design a realistic plan. If you don't take time to make these important decisions...nothing will happen. As I've said before, it has to be a plan you can live with! You are in complete control.

How to Design Your Plan

The following Perspective/Healthy Thinking Menu provides a list of things you can do to improve in this area. Based on your evaluation, select your top three priorities in this lifestyle category and transfer them to the recipe page. Then write one to three action items for each priority. An example is provided to help you.

Perspective/Healthy Thinking Menu

The One Thing

- ☐ I'm thinking and living with God as my highest priority.
- ☐ I am making intimacy with the Lord my greatest desire.
- ☐ need more time in the Word.
- ☐ I need more time in prayer.
- ☐ I need more time in meditation.
- ☐ I need more time in worship.

Attitudes

☐ I am building new healthy attitudes.

☐ I am securing my identity in Christ.

☐ I am developing a body image in sync with God's perspective of me.

☐ I have a "small steps" perspective…small stuff counts and adds up!

Self-Talk

☐ Identify your negative messages.

☐ Replace them with truth using trigger talk:

    ☐ Index cards   ☐ Tapes & CDs   ☐ Memorization

People Power

☐ Healthy Role Models for your lifestyle area.

☐ Mature Spiritual Mentors for your spiritual walk.

☐ Positive Motivators who can help you along the way.

☐ A personal coach, exercise or accountability partner.

Goal Evaluation

☐ What are my goals?

☐ Do they honor God?

☐ Do I have realistic expectations?

☐ Am I submitting and surrendering them to God?

☐ NOW…write them down!

Using Other Resources

☐ Journal for insight.

☐ Log for success.

☐ Listen to audio resources.

☐ Use and re-use this eight-week study guide.

My Perspective/Healthy Thinking Recipe

PRIORITY

ACTION

#1 __Self Talk__

Identify the lies I believe & replace
with truth.
Listen to my self talk CD everyday!!
Write my trigger talk & post in bathroom.

#2 _____

_____

_____

_____

#3 _____

_____

_____

_____

#4 _____

_____

_____

_____

PERSONAL REFLECTION

Answer the following questions on your own or with your group:

1. What lies do you believe that are most destructive in your life?

2. How do you continue to cultivate these lies in your life?

3. Who or what else helps foster these lies?

4. What can you begin doing right now to diminish their power in your life?

5. What healthy affirmation or scripture would help erase and replace one or more of those lies?

BUILD A STRONG SPIRITUAL FOUNDATION

Meditate on the following scripture and answer the corresponding questions:

"Do not be conformed to this world, but be transformed by the renewing of your mind." —Romans 12:2

1. How do we transform our minds?

2. Write down the three ways we learn:

   a. _____

   b. _____

   c. _____

3. Who are your positive role models?

   _____

   _____

   _____

4. What do you need to spend time imitating and repeating in order to transform your thinking?

"For what I am doing, I do not understand;
for I am not practicing what I would like to do,
but I am doing the very thing I hate." —Romans 7:15

1. Do you ever feel like Paul in your battle of the flesh?

2. Does his statement encourage or discourage you? Why?

3. As you continue to read in Romans chapter 7, what hope does Paul give you for this ongoing battle?

"But I say, walk by the Spirit, and you will not carry out the
desire of the flesh. But the fruit of the Spirit is love, joy, peace,
patience, kindness, goodness, faithfulness, gentleness and self-
control; against such things there is no law.
—Galatians 5:16; 22-23

1. How do you know when you are walking in the Spirit?

2. What changes can you make in your life to ensure you are walking in the Spirit more often than not?

NOURISH YOUR SPIRIT

Spiritual life-changing victory requires daily nourishment. Continue to nourish your spirit daily in four ways:

1. Pray as if it is the air you breathe.

This week, in addition to praying the prayer below, write your own prayer using a key scripture that will help erase and replace at least one of the lies you are believing.

Your written prayer:

2. Nourish your soul and spirit with God's Word daily.

Memorize Romans 12:2 and Galatians 5:16 and repeat them at least twice each day.

3. Digest its truths through meditation.

Meditate on what it means to "be transformed by the renewing of your mind". Imagine what your life would be like if you no longer believed things which impact you negatively. What would freedom from those lies look and feel like? Imagine the victory and pray for God to help your mind focus constantly on His truth.

4. Practice the presence of God.

Imagine that each time you think a negative, self-defeating thought, Jesus is standing right in front of you, His hands on each side of your face, looking intently into your eyes and saying *STOP IT! I love you and you don't need to believe these lies any longer...I have made all things new!*"

PRAYER FOR WEEK THREE

Dear Lord, it amazes me when I look at how you designed my mind. Help me to be a better steward of my thoughts. I pray that you will bring your Word to my mind when I am believing my old lies and that your truth will erase and replace my old, destructive thinking. I choose to set my mind on things above. Please help me to address my thinking each and everyday and to understand how important this principle is to every aspect of my life. May your truth set me free from bondage to all area of unhealthy thinking and living. Teach me how to walk in the Spirit that I will not fulfill the desires of my flesh. In Jesus' name, Amen.

SUGGESTED READING – WEEK THREE

Read the following chapters in *Scale Down* and check off below:

☐ *Chapter 8: You Are What You Think*
  - God's Rx for a healthy mind
  - Positive modeling: observe, imitate and repeat
  - Setting Godly goals
  - The power of self talk

☐ *Chapter 9: Battle of the Flesh*
  - The Holy Spirit and Chocolate Milk…whaaaaat??
    Read pg 130
  - Choosing your path
  - The enemy—Satan or me?
  - Fruits of the victorious lifestyle

WEEK 4

Burning Fat to the Max

In This Section:

- Burning Fat to the Max
- Lifestyle Fitness
- Lifestyle Evaluations: Fat Management and Fitness

Follow-Along Outline:

View or listen to session four as you complete the blanks in this outline and jot down your own notes or thoughts in the margins. Then, complete the study guide assignments for this week at the end of this section individually or with your group.

Burning Fat Facts

- ☐ One pound of fat = 3,500 calories.
- ☐ One pound of muscle = 500 calories.
- ☐ One pound of water = 0 calories.
- ☐ The body is 65% water.
- ☐ A 140-pound person = 91 pounds of water.
- ☐ One pound of fat burns 3 calories per day.
- ☐ One pound of muscle burns up to 50 calories per day.
- ☐ You can EAT calories a lot faster than you can BURN them!

5 Fat Burning Factors:

1. Gender
2. Genetics
3. Nutrition
4. Exercise/Activity
5. Muscle Mass

Factors out of your control = _____ %

> Gender
> Genetics

Factors in your control = _____ %

> Nutrition
> Exercise/Activity
> Muscle Mass

Nutrition

Fuel Storage Facts:

1 gram of carbohydrate = 4 calories
1 gram of protein = 4 calories
1 gram of fat = 9 calories

If you have 100 excess calories of:

Carbohydrate – 75% stores as fat
Protein – 60% stores as fat
Fat – 96% stores as fat!

Supporting Your "RMR" (Resting Metabolic Rate)

RMR = the number of calories you burn in 24 hours doing nothing
NEVER eat less than your RMR

A very rough RMR estimate = Your weight X 10*

*(*Decrease to 9 if you are only moderately active and 8 if you rarely exercise)*

Eat to Burn

Eat like you have a 5 gallon gas tank in your body (fuel and burn all day long).

Eat for _____ energy.

Eat for _____ fat storage.

Get a reality check on _____.

Exercise / Activity

Move…Move…Move!

- Our normal activity is NOT normal!
- Your lifestyle needs to get into the act.
- The #1 way to burn fat…Aerobic activity.
- More is not always better. Give yourself time to get in shape.

Muscle Mass

Notching Up Your Metabolic Engine

- Fit muscles increase the fat-burning "lipolytic" enzymes.
- Fit muscles burn more calories at rest.
- Fit muscles increase your metabolism.

How Active Are You?

Level 0: Sedentary: rarely exercise and lifestyle is not active.

Level 1: Moderate: get purposeful activity 1 to 2 times per week.

Level 2: Above Average: slightly active– exercise 2-3 times per week.

Level 3: High: active lifestyle – exercise 4 to 5 times per week.

Lose One Pound of Fat per Week

- Determine your RMR and don't eat less!
- Go to "Calorie College."
- Create a calorie budget.
- Burn at least 500 activity calories daily.

Example: A 160-pound woman

Daily RMR calorie burn:	1,600
Daily Activity Caloric burn:	+ 500
Total 24-hour calorie burn:	2,100
Daily Caloric intake:	- 1,600
NET Caloric difference:	500

500 calories per day x 7 days = 3,500 calories
3,500 calories = ONE pound of FAT!

Lifestyle Fitness...Use It or Lose It!

Fitness Myths

No _____ . . . No _____!

Muscle turns to _____.

You have to _____ to be fit.

Total Fitness

- Strength
- Aerobic Endurance
- Flexibility

1. Strength

a. _____ are your body's engine.

b. One pound of muscle burns 50 calories per day.

c. Increase lipolytic, fat-burning enzymes.

d. You begin losing fitness in 48 to 72 hours.

SMALL STEPS to increasing your strength

Level 1: Abdominal workouts every other day.

Level 2: Abdominal plus legs every other day.

Level 3: Abs and Legs every other day; upper body alternate days.

2. Aerobic Endurance

Definition: In the presence of oxygen.

- Large muscle, sustained activity
- The breathing test
- Target heart rate
- Perceived exertion
- Cardiovascular benefit
- Fat burning benefit

Warm Up

Cool Down

F.I.T.

- Frequency
- Intensity
- Time

BENEFITS of aerobic endurance:

- Lowers body fat
- Improves cardiovascular fitness

- Enhances immunity
- Increases metabolism and energy
- Releases "feel good" hormones

3. Flexibility

Muscular flexibility improves:
- Posture
- Balance
- Skeletal health
- Joint and muscle health
- Appearance
- Overall performance

SMALL STEPS to increasing your flexibility:
Level 1: Warm & stretch before workouts.
Level 2: Stretch before & after every workout.
Level 3: Three or more stretch/posture sessions per week.

What's YOUR Excuse?

I don't have _____.

I don't have _____.

I don't know _____.

I can't afford a _____.

Change your negative self-talk

Example:

Old negative message: *"I can't wait until this workout is over."*
New healthy message: *"I am so thankful I have a body that can move!"*

Example:

Old negative message: *"Exercise bores me."*

New healthy message: *"I enjoy exercise and the way it makes me feel."*

Get your lifestyle in the act:

- Use the stairs instead of the elevator.
- Park at the back of the parking lot.
- Take a walk on your lunch break.
- Take walking visits with your friends.
- Do gardening or yard work.
- Pace when you have to wait for someone.
- Play ball with the kids or the dog.
- Take active outings like trips to the zoo.

Keep Yourself On Track

Establish _____ goals.

Use a log to track your _____.

_____ yourself when you accomplish a goal.

Tailor your program to your _____ and _____ _____.

Fight boredom with _____ like music and television.

Develop a _____ of workout partners.

Get the green light from your _____!

Evaluate Your Lifestyle

Fat Management and Fitness
Personal lifestyle evaluations

Truth

Remember, ignorance is not bliss! If you don't know what the problem is, it's hard to fix it. So now it's time to be totally honest with yourself in your fitness and fat management lifestyle areas.

How to take the evaluations

Spend about four to five minutes on each evaluation. Base your answers on your most consistent behavior or attitudes in the past three months.

- DON'T rate yourself based on any changes you've made in the last 4 to 6 weeks.
- DO rate yourself based on your first impression and move on.
- DON'T go back and "readjust" your answers if you don't like the score!
- DO remember… this is a reality check. Just face the truth and move on.

Now, it's time to face the music. Grab a pencil and be completely honest. No one has to see the results but you!

Lifestyle Evaluation – Fat Management

Based on the last three months, please rate yourself as:
0 = Almost Never   1 = Sometimes   2 = Often   3 = Always

_____ I feel in control of my food choices.

_____ I measure my size by how I look and feel, not the scale.

_____ I eat only when I'm hungry.

_____ I stop eating when I'm full.

_____ I understand why "calories count".

_____ I eat 4 to 5 small meals or snacks per day.

_____ I limit my junk food, fast food and desserts to less than 15% of my diet.

_____ I am happy with my body weight.

_____ I am happy with my size and shape.

_____ I can enjoy "fun food" without feeling guilty.

_____ I think about food only when I'm hungry.

_____ I can see myself eating and living in control.

_____ I walk or get purposeful exercise at least 4x per week.

_____ I am very aware of my choices and how they affect my body.

_____ I say "No" to the latest diets or supplements promising quick results.

_____ I know if I'm going to be lean, I have to take daily action.

_____ *Add the total of all scores*

Lifestyle Evaluation - Fitness

Based on the last three months, please rate yourself as:
0 = Almost Never   1 = Sometimes   2 = Often   3 = Always

_____ I crave activity and find ways to move more each day.

_____ I enjoy exercise and how it makes my body feel.

_____ I have high energy to do all the things I want and need to do.

_____ I make exercise and activity a priority in my life.

_____ I understand the need for aerobic, strength and flexibility training.

_____ I engage in aerobic activity 4 or more times per week.

_____ I take the stairs or park far away whenever I can.

_____ I monitor my heart rate and know I am exercising safely.

_____ I am injury-free and able to engage in most activities freely.

_____ Being healthy and fit is important to me.

_____ I listen to my body and know what it needs.

_____ I wear appropriate and quality shoes for exercise.

_____ I have a very active life and am moving throughout the day.

_____ I work out my major muscle groups 2-3 times each week.

_____ I can easily touch my toes without bending my knees.

_____ I maintain strong abdominal muscles.

_____ *Add the total of all scores*

How did you do?

Your success depends upon your ability to prioritize your goals, design a realistic plan and surrender it daily to God.

Design a FAT MANAGEMENT success recipe

You've evaluated your lifestyle. You've educated your mind. Now it's time to initiate a new plan. It's unrealistic to make too many changes all at once. You'll just burn out and give up. Your success depends upon your ability to prioritize your goals and design a realistic plan. If you don't take time to make these important decisions...nothing will happen. As I've said before, it has to be a plan you can live with! You are in complete control.

How To Design Your Plan

The following Fat Management Menu provides a list of things you can do to improve in this area. Based on your evaluation, select your top three priorities in this lifestyle category and transfer them to the recipe page. Then write one to three action items for each priority. An example is provided to help you.

Fat Management Menu

Increase Your Daily Calorie Burn

☐ Aerobic activity is #1

☐ An active lifestyle makes a difference

☐ Use an Activity Monitor like FitBit to accurately assess your activity

Decrease Your Daily Calorie Intake

☐ Read labels

☐ Find enjoyable substitutions

☐ Count calories for absolute truth

☐ Keep a food diary

☐ Use portion control

☐ Plan your snacks

☐ Shop for success

☐ Cut your losses

Get a Handle on Emotional Eating

☐ Identify your triggers

☐ Create new habits

☐ Tune into the hunger scale

☐ Legalize foods

☐ Discard old diet attitudes

☐ Learn to cut your losses

Increase Your Energy & Metabolism

☐ Practice the NutriMax 6 (see Nutrition Menu)

☐ Never eat less than your RMR!

☐ Fuel and burn all day long

Practice Healthy Thinking

☐ Identify your lies

☐ Rewrite your Self-Talk

☐ Listen to your tapes!

Practice "Trigger" Talk

☐ In the car

☐ On the potty

☐ Everywhere!

My Fat Management Recipe

PRIORITY   ACTION

#1 Decrease Intake   Count calories for a one month reality check
Pre-package healthy snacks on the go
Practice portion control. Use smaller plate.

#2 _____   _____

                      _____

                      _____

                      _____

#3 _____   _____

                      _____

                      _____

                      _____

#4 _____   _____

                      _____

                      _____

                      _____

Design a FITNESS success recipe

Now it's time to do the same thing in your lifestyle fitness category. You know the drill...pick three priorities and write an action plan. Let's get started!

Fitness Menu

Aerobic Fitness - The ultimate calorie burn

☐ Level 1:   15 to 20 minutes 3 times per week

☐ Level 2:   20 to 30 minutes 5 times per week

☐ Level 3:   30+ minutes 6-7 times per week

Strength & Toning – Tuning your body's engine

☐ Level 1:   Abdominal workouts every other day

☐ Level 2:   Abdominal plus Leg Toning every other day

☐ Level 3:   Add upper body 2-3x per week, plus abs & legs

Flexibility – Posture & prevention

☐ Level 1:   "Warm" & stretch tight muscles before workouts

☐ Level 2:   Stretch before & after every workout

☐ Level 3:   Three or more stretch and posture sessions per week

The Lifestyle – Movin' & Groovin'

☐ All activity counts. So move, move, move

☐ Never sit if you can stand…

☐ Never stand when you can walk.

Advanced Fitness

☐ Cross training to enhance overall fitness

☐ Interval training for variety & strength

☐ Specific sport-training & strengthening

☐ Distance running or competitive training

Aches, pains, & limitations

☐ Take care of "problems" first

☐ Prevention is essential – broken bodies slow you down!

☐ Seek the advice of professionals and follow that advice!

MY FITNESS RECIPE

PRIORITY   ACTION

#1 _____   _____

                  _____

                  _____

                  _____

#2 _____   _____

                  _____

                  _____

                  _____

#3 _____   _____

                  _____

                  _____

                  _____

How Long Does it Take to Burn 100 Calories?

Activity	Duration	Calories Burned*
Biking	15 min	96
In-line skating	15 min	104
Jogging (10min/mile)	10 min	113
Jumping rope	10 min	100
Walking (15 min/mile)	15 min	113

*Estimates based on a 130-pound female.

The more you weigh, the more you'll burn per minute

Recommended Fitness Resources

☐ Total body home fitness equipment: TOTAL GYM (see Resource section)

☐ Exercise videotapes by Karen Voight and Kathy Smith

☐ Posture/Pain resource: www.egoscue.com

PERSONAL REFLECTION

Answer the following questions on your own or with your group:

1. What is the most important principle you learned about how your body burns fat and how will you apply it to your life?

2. What did your Fat Management evaluation reveal about your weaknesses in this area?

3. What is your greatest challenge in the area of lifestyle fitness and how will you address that challenge?

4. How does your attitude and self-talk impact your fat management and fitness issues?

BUILD A STRONG SPIRITUAL FOUNDATION

Meditate on the following scripture and answer the corresponding questions:

On the other hand, discipline yourself for the purpose of godliness; for bodily discipline is only of little profit, but godliness is profitable for all things, since it holds promise for the present life and also for the life to come. —1 Timothy 4:7- 8

1. Does the fact that the Apostle Paul says "bodily discipline is only of little profit" mean that we should disregard it?

2. How can physical discipline help us build mental and spiritual discipline?

3. Do you think the people of Paul's day had to work at being lean and fit?

4 How will you find balance between the disciplines of body, soul and spirit?

NOURISH YOUR SPIRIT

Spiritual life-changing victory requires daily nourishment. Continue to nourish your spirit daily in four ways:

1. Pray as if it is the air you breathe.

This week, spend some time praising the Lord for the blessings of your body. Thank him if you are able to walk or do other activities without too much difficulty. Ask Him to help you worship Him and celebrate this great gift by moving more and getting more physically fit.

2. *Nourish your soul and spirit with God's Word daily.*

Before eating too many calories...feed yourself truth from God's Word. Feast on His powerful principles and let it transform you from the inside out.

3. *Digest its truths through meditation.*

Imagine and meditate on how you can glorify God by living a victorious lifestyle...one that increases your health, vitality and passion for ministry.

4. *Practice the presence of God.*

As you eat and burn like a car with a four gallon tank, walk or run to maximize fat burning or engage in strength training or flexibility exercises, imagine that the Lord is your workout partner. Just as we are encouraged by Paul to "work as unto the Lord", why not "workout as unto the Lord" as well?

PRAYER FOR WEEK FOUR

Heavenly Father, thank you for my body. Please forgive me for not caring for it as a precious gift from you. I desire to honor you in my body by eating, moving and living in ways that enhance my health and energy. Please help me to have a godly desire that pursues physical fitness without diminishing my commitment to spiritual fitness. Lord, I need to find the balance that only You can give. Show me how to transform my lifestyle to your glory. Amen.

SUGGESTED READING – WEEK FOUR

Read the following chapters in *Scale Down* and check off below:

☐ *Chapter 11: Burning Fat to the Max*
  - Finding your "one thing" for burning fat
  - The bottom line to your bottom line
  - Your body's three fuel sources
  - Five fat-burning factors
  - From knowledge to action in 4 steps

☐ *Chapter 14: Use It or Lose It...Lifestyle Fitness*
  - How to get started safely
  - Danna's TV workout

WEEK 5

You Are What You Eat

In This Section:

- The Nutri-Max 6
- The Nutri-Zap 4
- Simplifying Supplements...A Top 10 List
- Nutrition Evaluation and Plan

Follow-Along Outline:

View or listen to session five as you complete the blanks in this outline and jot down your own notes or thoughts in the margins. Then, complete the study guide assignments for this week at the end of this section individually or with your group.

Nutritional Basics

Your diet each day is composed of carbohydrates, protein and fat. A common question is how much a person should eat of each fuel source. These are the recommended ranges:

Percentage of total calories:

Carbohydrates	45 – 60 %
Proteins	15 – 30%
Fats	15 – 30%

Grams based on 2000 calories:

Carbohydrates   220 – 300 grams

Proteins   75 – 150s grams

Fats   33 – 55 grams

The Nutri-Max 6

Nutri-Max #1 – WATER

A quart low and running on steam

Wasted _____ - wasted _____

Headaches and hunger

The caffeine/water facts

Get the plastic out (don't refill plastic water bottles!)

Nutri-Max #2 – PLANT FOODS

The "real" carbohydrates

Antioxidant power

Phytochemicals

Fiber's many roles

Enzymes for life

Nutri-Max #3 – PROTEIN

How much is enough?

Where's the beef?

Fish facts

Other sources

Blood sugar balance

Nutri-Max #4 – ESSENTIAL FATS

The good
The essential
The bad
The ugly

Nutri-Max #5 – VITAL VITAMINS

Danna's Top-Ten Supplement List
1. High-Potency Vitamin-Mineral Complex
2. Super Green Foods
3. Essential Fatty Acids
4. Vitamin C
5. Garlic
6. Calcium/Magnesium
7. Vitamin E
8. Ginkgo Biloba
9. Green Tea
10. Milk Thistle

Nutri-Max #6: VITAMINS Z & X

Vitamin Z _____ – you can't live without it!

Vitamin X _____ - you need it even if you don't like it!

The Nutri-Zap 4

#1 Sugar

#2 White Flour

#3 Caffeine

#4 Artificial Sweeteners
   Saccharin
   Aspartame
   Splenda

Healthy alternatives
   Stevia - See www.mdvventures.com
   Xylitol - See www.globalsweet.com
   Lo Han - See www.easymuscle.com

Learn to Read Labels
   ☐ How many portions?
   ☐ How big are they?
   ☐ How many calories?
   ☐ How much fat and what kind?
   ☐ How much protein?
   ☐ How much fiber?
   ☐ What's the nutritional value?
   ☐ Is this food worth the "cost"?

Small Steps Add Up!
   • A 20% improvement for a lifetime is better than a 100% improvement for a few weeks or months!
   • Add more natural foods.

- Eat less packaged products.
- Keep it balanced.
- Remember…you ARE what you eat!

Evaluate Your Lifestyle

Nutrition
A personal lifestyle evaluation

It's now time to evaluate your nutrition. Spend about four to five minutes on the evaluation. Base your answers on your most consistent behavior or attitudes in the past three months.

- DON'T rate yourself based on any changes you've made in the last 4 to 6 weeks.
- DO rate yourself based on your first impression and move on.
- DON'T go back and "readjust" your answers if you don't like the score!
- DO remember… this is a reality check. Just face the truth and move on.

Now, it's time to face the music. Grab a pencil and be completely honest. No one has to see the results but you!

Lifestyle Evaluation: Nutrition

Based on the last three months, please rate yourself as:
0 = Never / Don't Know   1 = Sometimes   2 = Often   3 = Always

_____ I think about what I eat and how it impacts my health.

_____ I have high energy to do all the things I want and need to do.

_____ I read labels and choose many foods based on that information.

_____ I eat 2-3 servings of fruit each day.

_____ I eat 3-4 servings of vegetables each day.

_____ I choose whole grain products over more processed foods.

_____ I know how much fiber I'm eating daily.

_____ I drink 10 to 12 glasses of water daily.

_____ I eat breakfast every day.

_____ I eat a good source of protein at breakfast.

_____ I choose and eat lean protein with my lunch.

_____ I limit my "empty" calories to less than 15% of my total diet.

_____ I limit caffeine, other stimulants, and over the counter diet aids.

_____ I take a multi-vitamin supplement daily.

_____ I take an antioxidant supplement daily.

_____ I choose "healthy" fats in my diet like olive or Canola oil.

_____ *Add the total of all scores*

How did you do?

Your success depends upon your ability to prioritize your goals, design a realistic plan and surrender it daily to God.

Design a NUTRITION success recipe

Now that you've evaluated your nutrition and educated your mind, it's time to initiate a new plan. If you don't take time to make these important decisions... nothing will happen. As I've said before, it has to be a plan you can live with! You are in complete control. This is a very important category and an example is provided to help you.

Remember, you build a completely new body every seven years, including your skeleton. It can only be as strong as the supplies you give it to work with. So as you make decisions about how you will eat and live for a lifetime, keep in mind that you can't build a brick house out of straw; nor can you build a healthy body out of sugar!

An Example: "My Nutrition Recipe"

PRIORITY

ACTION

#1 Drink more water

Drink with meals

Carry bottle with me

#2 Eat more veggies

Keep stocked up - make it easy!

Order more salads

#3 Less poison!

Artificial sweeteners - Limit to 2-3 servings per week max!

Limit fast food to only 1x per week

#4 Increase FIBER

Start with high fiber & high protein breakfast everyday

Add beans and read labels for fiber content

Nutrition Menu

Wonderful Water

- ☐ 8 to 12 glasses per day
- ☐ Carry water with you
- ☐ Limit caffeinated beverages

Fiber-rich Fruits

- ☐ 3 to 4 fruits per day (Most servings ½ cup)
- ☐ Whole fruits instead of juice
- ☐ Variety is important

Fiber-rich Vegies

- ☐ 4 to 5 veggies per day (Most servings equal ½ cup)
- ☐ Quality counts...French fries don't!
- ☐ Frozen is as good as fresh

Quality Carbos

- ☐ Beans, bran and "brown"
- ☐ White bagels & pretzels don't count
- ☐ Whole grain on the label is the key
- ☐ Nuts in moderation

Powerful Proteins

- ☐ Always w/ breakfast & lunch
- ☐ Healthy shakes and bars
- ☐ Keep stocked with easy choices

Fabulous Fats - Omegas Rule!

- ☐ Increase Omega 3's the most – Fish, flaxseed, walnuts
- ☐ Omega 6's – Keep vegetable oils to a bare minimum
- ☐ Omega 9's - Choose olive oil over vegetable oil
- ☐ Nuts are okay – watch the cals
- ☐ Keep saturated fat 10% of total fat max!

Vital Vitamins

- ☐ Fill in your nutritional gaps
- ☐ Multi-vitamin & mineral in 2 doses
- ☐ Anti-Oxidants to fight free radicals
- ☐ Choose 5 from the top 10 list and be consistent.

Fuel & Burn

- ☐ Start with breakfast
- ☐ Eat like a car with a 4-gallon tank
- ☐ Stop when you're full
- ☐ Eat lighter at night

Pick Your "Poisons"

- ☐ Limit junk food & chemicals
- ☐ Fun food - no more than 15%
- ☐ Artificial sweeteners < 3 servings/week
- ☐ Limit sugar and caffeine

My Nutrition Recipe

PRIORITY   ACTION

#1 _____   _____

                         _____

                         _____

                         _____

#2 _____   _____

                         _____

                         _____

                         _____

#3 _____   _____

                         _____

                         _____

                         _____

PERSONAL REFLECTION

Answer the following questions on your own or with your group:

1. How are you doing? You've been working on your new lifestyle for a few weeks now. What do your lifestyle behaviors say about the changes you are (or aren't) making in the following areas:

   ☐ The quality of my nutrition says:

   ☐ The amount of food I eat says:

   ☐ The way I move and exercise says:

   ☐ The way I relax and sleep says:

   ☐ The way I respond to stress or worry says:

2. How do you feel about your progress thus far?

3. What changes or help will you pursue to continue to change your attitudes and behavior?

NOURISH YOUR SPIRIT

Meditate on the following scripture and answer the corresponding questions:

> *"Whether, then, you eat or drink or whatever you do, do all to the glory of God." —1 Corinthians 10:31*

1. Try to imagine every meal or snack you eat as if you are enjoying it with the Lord. How would that change your behavior?

2. How do we influence our motives and attitudes about food and our habits so that they do glorify God?

3. Imagine every food and drink that you ingest either building up your body or diminishing your health. Do we glorify God when we eat empty calories or unhealthy foods in excess?

NOURISH YOUR SPIRIT

Spiritual life-changing victory requires daily nourishment. Continue to nourish your spirit daily in four ways:

1. Pray as if it is the air you breathe.

Include in your prayers this week a focus on thankfulness for the incredible gift of taste and smell. Praise God for His wonderful provision of food to nourish our bodies. Surrender your battle with food to the Lord and ask Him to transform your thinking about food so that you eat to live rather than "live to eat" if that is a challenge for you. Ask Him to help you see your body from the inside out and come to a full realization that what you eat becomes your new body each day, week, month and year.

2. Nourish your soul and spirit with God's Word daily.

Look back at the scriptures that have been used so far in the program and in this study guide and pick one or two that you believe best feed your soul in the area of your lifestyle. Memorize those and study them in the context of their complete chapter for greater understanding.

3. Digest its truths through meditation.

Now, meditate on one or more of those verses this week. Ask the Lord to illuminate and animate those truths in your mind and spirit as you digest them more fully and allow them to transform your life.

4. Practice the presence of God.

Continue to focus on seeing the Lord with you at every meal and even as you sometimes struggle with the temptation of food. Realize His unconditional love for you and desire to help you grow in victory.

PRAYER FOR WEEK FIVE

Father God, I am so thankful that you have given me all I need to eat and live. I am thankful for the wonder of my five senses and for the great pleasure that smell and taste bring. I pray that I would not misuse this gift and eat more than my body needs or take in too many empty calories or foods that cause my body damage. Help me to see food as a source of nutrition first and joy second. Help me to enjoy and celebrate foods the way you originally made them. I choose to present my body as a living sacrifice to you. Be glorified in my habits and health. Amen.

SUGGESTED READING – WEEK ONE
Read the following chapter in *Scale Down* and check off below:

☐ *Chapter 12: You Are What You Eat*

This chapter is full of great nutritional information. Because everyone wants to know what and how to eat, it's important material. Here, you'll learn my basic philosophy, and in depth teaching about the NutriMax 6 and the NutriZap 4, fiber, protein, carbos, fats, water and more!

☐ *Extra Assignment:*

Buy a "Food Counts" book that includes fiber, calories, protein, carbohydrate and fat content information. There are many choices on the bookstore shelves. One I have used over the years is The Complete Book of Food Counts by Netzer. Calorie counting may seem like drudgery, but you only need to do it for about a month to reap the benefit for life. Go to "calorie college" and get a reality check on what you're really eating. Write down your regular meals and calculate the calories and nutritional value. We're creatures of habit and tend to eat a lot of the same things most of the time. This exercise is a real eye-opener and will give you valuable insight as you continue your lifestyle journey.

WEEK 6

You Are What You Don't Eat

In This Section:

- You Are What You DON'T Eat
- Overcoming Emotional Eating

Follow-Along Outline:

View or listen to session six as you complete the blanks in this outline and jot down your own notes or thoughts in the margins. Then, complete the study guide assignments for this week at the end of this section individually or with your group.

You Are What You Don't Eat

Do YOU eat ONLY when you are hungry?

> *"No temptation has overtaken you, but such as is common to man; and God is faithful, who will not allow you to be tempted beyond what you are able, but with the temptation will provide the way of escape also, that you will be able to endure it."*
> —1 Corinthians 10:13

> *"Therefore, my beloved, flee from idolatry."* —1 Corinthians 10:14

Grumbling in the Wilderness

"Who will give us meat to eat? We remember the fish, which we used to eat free in Egypt, the cucumbers and the melons and the leeks and the onions and the garlic, but now our appetite is gone. There is nothing to look at except all this manna."
—*Numbers 11:4-6*

Overcoming Emotional Eating

- ☐ Legalize food
- ☐ Tune in to the hunger scale
- ☐ Identify emotional eating triggers
- ☐ Change your self-talk
- ☐ Energize for self-control

Legalize Food

There are no "_____" foods.

I can eat this food _____.

So, I don't have to eat it _____.

And, I don't have to eat it _____.

I'm putting dangerous foods "_____".

I'm practicing "_____".

The Hunger Scale

At 1:   I am "STARVING!"

At 2:   I'm slightly hungry.

At 3:   I feel neutral.

At 4:   I'm physically satisfied.

At 5:   I'm "Thanksgiving" full.

When you feel like eating, ask yourself these questions:

☐ Am I really hungry?

☐ If not, what's really going on?

☐ And, what should I do instead...sleep?

☐ If yes, what will satisfy me?

Change Your Self-Talk

"I cannot stand feeling full. It is absolutely unbearable, so I never do it!"

Identify Emotional Eating Triggers

The EVENT/FOOD Connection:

☐ TV

☐ Ballgames

☐ Parties

☐ Other

HALT! Are you:

- ☐ Hungry?
- ☐ Angry?
- ☐ Lonely?
- ☐ Tired?

Energize for self-control

The positive energy cycle

- ☐ Get adequate sleep
- ☐ Manage stress
- ☐ Eat and drink for maximum energy
- ☐ Exercise for maximum energy

Five Tips for Reducing Calories

#1 Daytime eating

- If most people simply ate one-half their usual volume of food from 6 p.m. until bedtime, they would _____ _____.

#2 Substitution

- Find _____ and _____ options that still taste good!
- Follow the 80% satisfaction rule.

#3 Meal Replacements

- Find a _____, _____ or _____ that you like for busy days or "emergencies".

#4 Portion Control

- Simply eat smaller _____!
- Quit the "clean plate club".
- Eat the same...just eat less!
- Use a _____ plate.

#5 Calories

- Get a good "food counts" book.
- Learn to conceptualize calories.
- _____ your favorite foods.
- If it's worth eating...it's worth counting.
- Your body is a perfect calorie counting machine.
- Go to "_____ _____" for one month.

Hints on Conceptualizing Calories

- ☐ Check out the labels on frozen foods.
- ☐ Get familiar with serving sizes.
- ☐ When in doubt, measure.
- ☐ Err conservatively – Count HIGH!
- ☐ Be honest with yourself.

Equate serving sizes with:

- ☐ A deck of cards = 3 oz. of meat
- ☐ Your fist = 1 cup of rice or potatoes
- ☐ Your thumb = 1 oz of cheese or candy

Decrease Your Caloric Intake
Learn to:

- _____

- _____

- _____

- _____

- _____

Words for the walk

Physical Check Points
- ☐ Find creative ways to eat fewer calories daily.
- ☐ Develop a more active lifestyle.
- ☐ Eat for maximum energy and health.

Soul Check Points
- ☐ Discover the lies you believe.
- ☐ Replace them with truth.
- ☐ Observe, imitate and repeat healthy thinking and living.
- ☐ Get and be an excellent role model.

Spiritual Check Points
- ☐ Pray as if it's the air you breathe.
- ☐ Feed your soul with God's Word.
- ☐ Digest its truth through meditation.
- ☐ Practice the presence of God.

PERSONAL REFLECTION

Answer the following questions on your own or with your group:

1. What three changes would make the biggest difference in your nutrition if you chose to implement them on a daily basis?

   1. _____

   2. _____

   3. _____

2. What are your biggest emotional eating triggers?

3. What principles, scriptures or techniques will you use to address those triggers?

4. Choose three to four calorie-cutting strategies that you will try to implement this week and write them here:

   1. _____

   2. _____

   3. _____

   4. _____

BUILD A STRONG SPIRITUAL FOUNDATION

Meditate on the following scripture and answer the corresponding questions:

All things are lawful for me, but not all things are profitable. All are lawful for me, but I will not be mastered by anything. Food is for the stomach and the stomach is for food, but God will do away with both of them. —1 Corinthians 6:12

1. If everything is lawful or permissible, how do you make the right choices?

2. Do you feel like anything in your life has mastery over you? If so, what is it?

3. Why does Paul tell us that God will do away with both food and the stomach?

4. How do we get ourselves to choose God's glorification instead of our immediate gratification?

"No temptation has overtaken you but such as is common to
man; and God is faithful, who will not allow you to be tempted
beyond what you are able, but with the temptation will provide
the way of escape also, so that you will be able to endure it.
Therefore, my beloved, flee from idolatry.
—*1 Corinthians 10:13, 14*

1. Is food an idol in your life and if "yes", how?

2. How can you change that and how can you "flee" from that
   form of idolatry?

"Abide in Me, and I in you. As the branch cannot bear
fruit of itself unless it abides in the vine, so neither can you
unless you abide in Me. I am the vine, you are the branches;
he who abides in Me and I in him, he bears much fruit,
for apart from Me you can do nothing. "If you abide in Me, and
My words abide in you, ask whatever you wish, and it will be
done for you. My Father is glorified by this, that you bear much
fruit, and so prove to be My disciples." —John 15:4-5; 7-8

1. What do you think it means to "abide" in Christ?

2. Are there ever times when you feel "disconnected" from Him?

3. What kind of "fruit" do we bear when we abide?

NOURISH YOUR SPIRIT

Spiritual life-changing victory requires daily nourishment. Continue to nourish your spirit daily in four ways:

1. Pray as if it is the air you breathe.

Choose one or two of the scripture in this weeks study section and personalize them in a prayer to the Lord. Ask Him to show you how to flee the idolatry of food. Focus in on how much more satisfying and enriching the power of prayer is over the desires of the flesh. Ask that he transform your mind to truly believe that truth.

2. Nourish your soul and spirit with God's Word daily.

Study in the areas of your greatest weaknesses and surrender your heart and mind in the process, asking God to reveal His truth to you in a very personal way. Look for practical ways to implement these truths into your life.

3. Digest its truths through meditation.

Meditate on the scriptures you are praying this week. Say them over and over. See yourself submitting to those truths. Imagine the glory you bring to God when you surrender your battle to Him and lift your praises to Him as He gives you victory in your struggles.

4. Practice the presence of God.

One of the hardest things to do is to imagine God with you when you are stumbling with temptation or sin. Yet, the truth is...He IS! So, this week imagine His presence. And, rather than respond in shame, respond in surrender and petitions for His divine intervention in the midst of trials.

PRAYER FOR WEEK SIX

Heavenly Father, I am so thankful that You love me for who I am in Christ rather than for how I behave. I delight to do your will, Lord. Please help me to run to You, rather than from You in the midst of my temptations. Show me where I idolize food, comfort or other "things" over You. Show me the "way of escape" and lead me down the path of the Spirit where I can experience the fruit of the Spirit on a daily basis. In Jesus' name, Amen.

SUGGESTED READING – WEEK SIX

Read the following chapters and check off below:

- ☐ **Chapter 10: Overcoming Emotional Eating**
  - Do you live to eat?
  - What does healthy eating look like?
  - Legalizing food
  - Getting in tune with your hunger
  - Identifying your eating triggers

- ☐ **Chapter 14: You Are What You DON'T Eat**
  - *"Oh my goodness, that's why I'm fat!"*, exclaimed Pamela.
  - What lifestyle revelations have you had?

- Effective calorie control without dieting
- Meal planning, dining strategically and surviving special occasions
- Shopping for success
- 52 calorie-busting ideas

☐ *Chapter 17: Words for the Walk*

Congratulations! You've made it to the last chapter of the book. The section titles are Victory at Last and the Joy Factor. It's short, but important. Continued blessings on your Scale Down journey.

I also recommend the following two books:

☐ *Idols of the Heart* by Elyse Fitzpatrick
☐ *Classic Christianity* by Bob George

WEEK 7

Healthy Eating and Cooking Ideas

In This Section:

- Keys to Calorie Control
- Healthy Eating and Cooking Ideas
- Favorite Recipes

Whether you are participating in a group or going through this program alone, now is the time to begin to seriously implement many of the nutritional concepts we've been addressing. For this reason, we have taken many of the expanded nutritional concepts from the book that were not covered in the CD or DVD program and reintroduced them here for your convenience. We have also added extra ideas and recipes to foster more success.

Implement This Idea

When reading through this section, take a highlighter or red pen and highlight those ideas that appeal to you. Then, put those items on your shopping list.

As I write this week's study information, I am on a plane to Virginia Beach, Virginia to appear on *The 700 Club* with Pat Robertson and talk about the concepts from *Scale Down*. And, guess what this particular airline is serving on our almost five hour flight across the country? Here goes:

First, we are offered all assortments of beverages (I already had a bottle of water with my two packets of "EmergenC" mixed in, so I opted for hot water to make my own tea). To compliment our beverage, we get a package of vanilla wafers that have 200 calories and not even a smidge of protein or fiber. I was so glad I brought a protein energy bar as my plane left at 7:45 am and I didn't have time for breakfast before leaving.

Then, an hour later, we were promised a more substantial snack box. I thought perhaps they'd include an apple and some cheese. The closest we got to cheese was the "Cheese Whiz" type filling in the Ritz Crackers. To compliment all the carbos, we got a package of Oreos AND some Gummie-like Jello candies.

Can you say "blood sugar crisis"? Good news is after 30 minutes the plane is very quiet. Everyone who ate that snack is sleeping it off. Thank goodness they did give me one half ounce of peanuts. I'll be a little hungry when I hit my destination, but still high energy and ready for a "real" meal.

One of the key things you've been learning is that to have lifestyle victory and to avoid blood crashes, you need to BE PREPARED. So, dig into this information and put some of it into action. And , the next time you're a mile high on a nutritionally challenge airline...you'll be ready!

Keys to Calorie Control

Planning for Success

Your success in developing a healthy approach to cutting calories depends on your willingness to change your old ways of doing things and plan, plan, plan. The best way to avoid eating disaster is to be prepared! The following ideas will ensure you are prepared for anything!

Be Prepared

- Plan all meals beforehand
- Dine out strategically and know your options
- Learn how to survive special occasions
- Practice "calorie-busting"
- Shop for success

Meal Planning

It will take a little time for you to develop a lifestyle of eating that is both satisfying and effective in helping you burn off excess fat. There is no single plan that will work for everyone. You must plan your eating based on your likes, dislikes, lifestyle and objectives.

Each time you decide to have a meal or snack, you must decide what choices will best meet all your objectives. The more satisfied you are after a meal, the better chance you will not overeat later. Consider these factors:

- What sounds good?
- How hungry am I?
- How many calories have I burned?
- How many calories will I burn?
- How many calories can I afford to eat?
- What do I feel like?
- Is there adequate protein and fiber to stabilize my blood sugar?

Plan with a Purpose

Most people find that they are satisfied with one or two main breakfast options, several lunch choices and a wide variety at dinner. To help you get your lifestyle in check, try to determine 2 to 3 healthy breakfasts, 3 to 4 lunch choices and 5 to 6 dinner options that fit with your personal tastes and move you toward your lifestyle goals. Write these down in a notebook or on index cards and rotate the choices over the next several weeks. Make sure that you are always getting a good source of protein and fiber at breakfast and lunch. And, of course, dinner is the meal that needs to be smallest, so decrease your portions and eliminate the "unnecessary" such as bread. Keep snacks to 100 to 200 calories maximum. Whenever possible, try to find foods that have some fiber or protein as well to help stabilize your blood sugar.

The following ideas may be helpful in making better meal and snack choices. You don't have to write out detailed eating plans to lose excess fat, but you do need to be purposeful, wise and committed to eating for maximum energy and never taking in more calories than you burn.

Breakfast

As you learned in the NutriMax 6, breakfast is the meal that "jump-starts" your metabolism for the day. It's important to fuel up within the first two hours of waking even if you don't feel hungry. In fact, some studies indicate that eating breakfast can increase your metabolism by up to 10%! Try to include protein and fiber with each meal. Avoid simple sugars and caffeine early in the day to ensure a stable blood sugar.

Lunch

Lunch should be your most substantial meal. It needs to sustain you through your busy day. It will impact your hunger in those dangerous hours in the evening. Lunch is an excellent time to include a little more protein in your diet through lean poultry and fish or lots of beans and legumes. Planning will ensure you make healthy choices. Include leftovers from previous dinners or choices from healthy restaurants.

Snack Options

Remember it's best to fuel and burn with frequent, small meals or snacks all day long for maximum energy. It's good to always have healthy snack options with you, such as a sturdy piece of fruit, like an orange or apple, and a bottle of water for a quick snack when you're on the go. I also like good energy bars with adequate protein and a little fat. They satisfy my hunger and sweet cravings and the protein stabilizes my blood sugar. The important thing is to avoid reaching "1" on the hunger scale. Another good strategy is to have "pre-portioned" baggies or containers with nuts, dried fruit or other snacks that are quickly satisfying. But, *if not pre-measured,* many snacks turn into excess calories and ultimately excess fat.

Dinner Options

In our culture, dinner has traditionally been our main meal. But, in reality, if you think about it, there is no need to fuel up for rest, relaxation or sleep. Dinner should be taken as early in the evening as possible and kept fairly light. Consider it roughly one-fifth of your daily calories or a maximum of about 400 to 500 calories on an active day. If you are an evening "muncher", make dinner even lighter.

Take the challenge and lose a pound a week!

It is my personal belief that most people would lose weight very easily if they simple cut the amount of calories they eat in their last four hours of each day in half. For most that would be at least 500 calories per day. That is one pound of fat per week and 52 pounds in a year. Make sense? Why not test my theory on yourself?

You'll find many healthy food suggestions in this section, but not very extensive menu plans. That is because I do not believe that telling people exactly how to eat is a good long-term plan for losing weight and keeping it off. It's highly unlikely that you will eat based on prepared meal plans for the rest of your life. My purpose is to educate you so that you can make food choices that will work for you. Make your choices based on the energy, body size and lifestyle you desire.

Keep it simple

Keep your healthy eating as simple as possible to ensure success. Don't underestimate the very simple, yet profound principle I have been teaching you from "Day One"...Eat a little less and burn a little more each and every day. And, when you find yourself in circumstances where you have little or no choice, remember that the very simple technique of portion control is always a helpful tool.

Shopping for Success

To keep your calories under control you must have a wide variety of excellent choices always at hand. Plan a day when you can spend an extra 30 or 40 minutes in the grocery store "exploring". You will be amazed at some of the fantastic new foods that are great alternatives to some of the old, more fattening favorites. Shop with a mission and make sure you never enter a grocery store hungry! Reading labels accurately is also very important. Don't ever buy anything in a bag, can or box without reading the label first!

Create a shopping list

Try to have a working grocery list with you at all times. When you think of an item that will help you refine your lifestyle, add it to the list. So, do you have a piece of paper handy, because you'll probably find a few items you'll want to put on your list in the next several pages!

The next time you need to visit the store, shop the perimeter FIRST, focusing on fresh fruits, veggies and healthy protein choices as the staple of your diet. Then, you can move on to finding an assortment of healthy packaged and convenience food choices. Make sure you have something in each of the following categories:

1. Fast breakfast, lunch and dinner options for when time is an issue

2. Fruits and veggies that need little preparation (baby carrots, apples, bananas)

3. Healthy and quick snacks or meal replacements (Balance bars, nuts, canned soup)

4. Bottled water (always)

5. Calorie/portion controlled treats (low fat ice cream bars, graham crackers and healthy frozen meals)

Dining Out Strategically

Dining out doesn't need to be an exercise in frustration where you feel like you've lost total control. By understanding nutrition basics, you can eat almost anywhere healthfully. Don't be afraid to ask for what you want; you are the customer.

Review restaurant choices

Write down all the restaurants you visit at least once each month. Determine what you believe to be the best choices and order those. Take the time to go to their websites for nutritional information, or ask for their information next time you are there. Just be sure and check it out BEFORE you order or you could get an upset stomach! A great resource is a book, *Eating Out Food Counter* by Natow & Heslin.

9 Ways To Dine Out Strategically

1. Decide beforehand what kind of food choices you will make.

2. Be assertive when requesting your food servings and preparation.

3. Consider sharing or ordering half-portions.

4. Ask how much fat is used in preparation and if necessary, ask for it to be reduced.

5. Have the waiter remove your plate as soon as you feel full.

6. Never go out when you're a "one" on the hunger scale.

7. Avoid the words fried, breaded, creamed, au gratin and a la mode!

8. Remember that white sauces are always richer than red.

9. Ask for your salad tossed with a half portion of salad dressing or pasta with half the sauce.

Move on when you blow it

When you eat too much or make poor choices...don't sabotage your entire day (or week) by caving in emotionally. Make a mental note of how uncomfortable you feel when you've eaten too much or how badly you feel when your energy plummets. Remind yourself how great you feel when you make better choices. Then...GET OVER IT! If we simply learn to cut our losses and get back on track, the blow outs will rarely have a huge impact.

Surviving Special Occasions

Holidays and special occasions almost always include high calorie foods. Whenever you attend a party or special event there are several strategies that can help you take control of your calorie intake. First, never, never starve yourself beforehand. That is a sure way to increase the chance of a blowout! Here are seven more strategies for surviving special occasions:

1. Start the day with breakfast and practice the NutriMax 6. High energy means less cravings!

2. Offer to bring a low calorie snack or contribution to the meal.

3. Brush your teeth just before the event. Food just doesn't taste as good right after brushing.

4. At parties, stand away from the goodies and focus on socializing.

5. Picture everything on a buffet table as at least 100 calories for every three bites. It adds up fast.

6. Drink lots of water or club soda to keep you hydrated and full.

7. Don't hesitate to leave food on your plate. If it isn't awesomely delicious, don't finish it.

Cutting Calories Daily

Calories add up fast

There are unlimited ways to reduce calories and fat from your food. From buttering your toast to preparing a gourmet meal, you can use creative techniques to create delicious and healthier alternatives. You can find many excellent light-cooking magazines or cookbooks at any local bookstore. Never forget that every calorie counts. If you creatively save 200 calories each day, you could be 20 pounds lighter in a year!

Concentrated calories

There are some foods we need to eat sparingly because they are so high in calories such as cheese, olives, avocados and nuts. While they are satisfying and healthful in small amounts, it is very easy to eat too many. Flavor your foods with these rich treats, but try not to make them a substantial part of your meal or snack. I do recommend nuts as snacks since they are such a great source of protein, fiber and healthy fat...BUT...measure out servings of one ounce and stop at that!

It goes without saying that other high calorie "fun foods" like candy, cookies and pastries add up fast. There are no forbidden foods, yet these rich and satisfying treats can make a big dent in your calorie bank account. I encourage you to get tuned into how much fat and calories are really in that mud pie and chocolate cheesecake they serve at your favorite restaurant. The truth alone will scare you into sharing your dessert and even leaving a few bites on the plate.

Healthy Eating & Calorie Busting Ideas

When you go on a traditional weight loss diet, you are given a list of foods you can and cannot eat and often the amount that is acceptable. That's great, if you follow it to a "T" because there is no room to fail. But, even if the diet works, you still have to figure out how to eat in the real world and keep the weight off. The reason I am so opposed to structured eating plans is because we are all so different. Making a lifestyle change may be a little more work up front and take a little longer to get in the "groove", but for those who are willing to do the work, the results will be long-lasting.

That is why I encourage you to take a some time to think about your eating challenges. It is helpful if you can identify when and where you have your greatest struggles. For many people, it is toward the end of the day. But, you may start the day of wrong with too much coffee, simple carbohydrates or no breakfast at all. Whatever your issues, identify them and create a strategy for addressing them.

The lists below may help you deal with some of your key areas. Take a highlighter and mark the suggestions that appeal to you. Then, take action and implement them.

Calorie-Busting at Breakfast

1. Eat your toast with jam and no butter or margarine.
2. On those rare occasions that you DO have pancakes, waffles or French toast – avoid using butter and just top them with reduced sugar syrup or jam. Pancakes are generally the lowest calorie choice. Make your own in a nonstick pan.
3. Scramble 1 yolk and 2 egg whites and save 120 calories!
4. Make an omelet with egg whites or egg-substitutes and add lots of your favorite chopped vegetables for flavor and fiber.

5. Read the labels on all bread, bagel and muffin packages to find the healthiest, low calorie, high fiber choice. Oroweat makes some of the best.

Calorie-Busting Snacks

1. There are many tasty low calorie popcorn choices. Be sure to read the portion size accurately.
2. Try frozen grapes or blueberries for a healthy snack.
3. Can't resist your occasional potato chip? Try Baked Lays – they're wonderful. Or buy a single one-ounce bag of your very favorite kind, sit down and slowly eat all 150 calories!
4. Mix 1/2 oz nuts (90 calories) with a half sliced apple. You'll be satisfied and fibered up!
5. Hard candy or mints are low in calories and satisfy the sweet tooth. They also take about 3-4 minutes to eat.
6. Graham crackers with a thin layer of peanut butter and warm herbal tea satisfy sweet cravings with less sugar and fat.
7. Avoid the guacamole and stick with low calorie salsa. If you can't resist the avocado, mix it with generous amounts of salsa and fresh tomatoes. And use carrots or celery for dipping between the one ounce of chips you've pre-measured!
8. Use cheese as a condiment, leave it off your sandwiches and burgers and cut the amount in recipes in half and avoid snacking on this dangerously high fat morsel.
9. High fat chips and buttery crackers can pile on calories quickly. Always pre-measure (or mentally calculate the amount) before you eat. If you can't be satisfied with one once, avoid them.

Calorie-Busting When Eating Out

1. Order one Caesar salad and one plain mixed salad and toss together to lower the calories and fat. Or, just ask the waiter to cut the dressing in half before they toss your salad!

2. Bypass fatty salad-bar extras such as sunflower seeds, high-fat croutons, and chow mein noodles and bacon bits. All those extras could add several hundred calories to your meal!

3. Carry your own reduced fat salad dressings. There are too many tasty and healthy dressings now available to ever settle for high fat choices.

4. Order an appetizer as an entrée at restaurants that serve huge portions. Light soup or salad and a small appetizer provides plenty of calories.

5. Flank steak, London Broil or filet mignon are the lower fat steak choices. As for the smallest option and eat about 4 ounces. Take the rest home.

6. Order pizza with a thin crust, 1/3 less cheese (or light cheese) and lots of veggies. Save about 100 to 150 calories per slice.

7. Always select "red" sauce versus "white" with your pasta. White sauce is usually high in cream, which means fat! Don't hesitate to order your sauce on the side. You can also ask them to prepare it with less oil.

8. Order a baked potato with the condiments on the side instead of French fries. New potatoes taste great and require less butter since they are moister than bakers.

9. Drain oily sauce from Chinese meals by lifting the food from the serving dish onto your plate with chopsticks or a fork.

10. Research all your regular fast food restaurants on line and pull up their nutritional information. Determine what the

healthiest choices are and be ready to order those next time you drive through. (Go to www.google.com and just put in the name of the restaurant and you will almost always get a list that will include their website with all the information you need. Be prepared to be shocked if you've never researched the calorie content of your favorite fast foods!)

Healthy Cooking Tips

1. Brown ground turkey or lean beef in a nonstick pan; then drain with hot water in a colander to remove excess fat.

2. Pre-cook your baked potatoes in the microwave for 5 to 8 minutes and the place in a 500-degree oven for about 10 minutes to make them fluffy. Don't forget to eat the skin!

3. Buy low-fat spaghetti sauces and add fresh onion, mushrooms, peppers and zucchini to increase the fiber and give it a homemade taste.

4. Make your own low-fat burritos. Buy low-fat tortillas, canned black beans, fresh cilantro and tomatoes and you've got a great source of protein and fiber.

5. Buy small packages of fresh herbs to add to many recipes for extra flavor. Food should never be bland – experiment!

6. Buy boneless, skinless chicken tenders and cook enough for a whole week. Throw them in salads, soups, pita bread, burritos, stir-fry or whatever!

7. Try a variety of low or nonfat marinades that are on the market to enhance any chicken, turkey or beef dish.

8. Use grains like couscous, kashi or brown rice as a base for many different meals such as:
   - Chili with cornbread
   - Petite peas and diced chicken tenders
   - Stir-fried veggies
   - London broil and grilled peppers, onions and sweet potatoes

9. Bake a sweet potato and mix in a small amount of light butter and 2 teaspoons of brown sugar. It's satisfying and packed with antioxidants and lots of fiber.

10. Buy fresh pastas and toss with a tablespoon of olive oil and one tablespoon of seasoned Feta cheese crumbled very small. Add fresh herbs.

11. Create your own lower fat salad dressing by mixing a flavored vinegar with your favorite higher fat dressing.

12. Sauté foods in chicken or vegetable broth, tomato juice or wine for lots of flavor and low calories!

13. Keep olive oil in a spray bottle to lightly coat cookware.

14. Make your own taco shells by hanging soft tortillas directly over the racks in your oven and baking at 400 degrees until crisp.

15. Refrigerate homemade soups overnight. Skim off the fat on top in the morning and saves tons of calories!

16. Cook rice, couscous and other grains in chicken broth and NO butter. It tastes great!

17. Thicken cream sauces with 1 percent milk and cornstarch instead of butter and flour.

18. Trim visible fat from meat and remove the skin from all poultry.

19. Use cocktail sauce or lemon juice instead of tartar sauce on fish.

20. Reduce the amount of meat or poultry in your fajitas, casseroles or other dishes and increase the vegetables, rice or beans.

21. Make your own eggplant or vegetable lasagna with low fat or less cheese.

22. Choose BBQ chicken instead of pork or beef. Remove the skin before baking your own.

23. Fresh herbs and feta cheese flavor up pasta without all the oils.

Lighter Choices

1. Switch from canned bakes beans made with pork to vegetarian varieties.

2. Never eat high fat ice cream. There are too many excellent low fat and nonfat alternatives. You'll potentially save hundreds of calories.

3. Check out the wide variety of dehydrated soups. Many are low in fat and very high in fiber. They are also easy to take to work. (Do watch for high sodium content and use in moderation.)

4. Croissants contain about 300 calories from fat. They're not worth it! Stick with your favorite fresh bread.

5. Use less low fat mayonnaise in tuna or chicken salad by adding a little low fat dressing such as S&W rice vinegar.

6. Opt for light-meat poultry instead of dark meat. Never eat the skin.

7. Artichokes with low fat mayonnaise or low calorie dips are nutritious and delicious. Try nonfat plain yogurt for your dip recipes also.

8. All tortillas are not equal. Read the labels and buy the smaller, lower fat and no lard selections.

9. Avoid buying highly processed and fatty luncheon meats like bologna, hotdogs and salami. Instead eat lean chicken and turkey.

10. Eat a turkey sandwich instead of chicken salad. (Save 200 to 300 calories.)

11. Choose albacore tuna packed in water instead of oil. (You'll get your Omega 3 fatty acids, too!)

12. Eggnog-flavored coffee creamer is a lot less calories than eggnog. Make a fresh cup of coffee with special flavor for dessert.

13. Reduce the amount of butter, mayonnaise, and other spreads on your breads, rolls, etc. The spread should totally blend into the surface of your food. Scrape off any excess with your knife before you take the first bite. You could save hundreds of calories per week changing this one habit and be 10 – 20 pounds leaner in a year!

14. Choose rolls instead of high fat biscuits.

15. Leave the cheese off your sandwich and add tomatoes, cucumbers or pickles.

16. Learn how to read labels correctly for fat and calorie content. Try to select snacks and desserts that are no more than 30 percent fat. Warning: Check out the serving size – it's often very small.

17. Love cheese? Select Parmesan, low fat mozzarella. Buy sharper cheeses for more flavor and use less.

18. Avoid regular mayonnaise especially if you are mixing it with something. Cut low fat mayonnaise with Dijon mustard to decrease the calories and increase the flavor.

Calorie-Busting Desserts

1. Sprinkle nuts on top of homemade desserts as a "flavoring" instead of mixing in the batter where the full flavor and texture may get lost.

2. Order one dessert for everyone at your table and share!

3. Substitute applesauce for some of the oil in your favorite recipes. Replace the oil with the exact amount of applesauce.

4. Look for recipes that use cocoa powder (which is no fat) in place of chocolate.

5. Order low fat, decaf lattes, cappuccino and other low calorie specialty drinks instead of dessert.

6. Sip low calorie hot cocoa to satisfy a chocolate craving.

7. Angel food cake can be dressed up in many ways for a non-fat dessert. Try making a chocolate angel food – yum!

8. Lower fat cookies include biscotti, vanilla-filled wafers, Oreo's and meringues. Read the labels.

9. Low fat frozen yogurt with special sauce or flavor is a wonderful treat. Try fruit sorbet with berries.

10. Once a week, go ahead and simply indulge in your favorite dessert, but eat only a third or a half of your usual portion.

Healthy Eating

Despite my aversion to creating eating plans, I do understand that many of you would like some ideas for getting enough protein, fiber and other key nutrients in your diet. I've included some of my favorite meal and snack choices that I eat on a regular basis. In some cases, I've included specific brands.

At the very end of this chapter, I've also added nine recipes that have been shared by many friends or clients. There is an abundance of healthy cookbooks on the market today. Not only do they include excellent recipes, but you can learn creative ways to cut calories in some of your favorite recipes by following some of their substitution principles.

Protein/Fiber Breakfast Choices

Protein Shake	400 calories/ Protein 16g/ Fiber 11g
Hard boiled egg	1 large/ 75 calories/ Protein 7g
Egg Beaters	¼ cup 100 calories /Protein 7g
Custard	150 calories/Protein 12g
Oat Bran Cereal (cooked)	1/3 cup uncooked/ 140 cals/ Protein 8g/ Fiber 7g
Bob's Red Mill Cereal	1/4 cup dry/ 140 cals/ Protein 6g/ Fiber 5g *(Order online: bobsredmill.com)*
Bran Flakes	1 cup 110 calories/ Protein 8g / Fiber 4-6g
Peanut Butter	(1Tb) 100 calories/ 4.5g protein
Oroweat Lt Whole Wheat Bread	2 slices/ 80 calories/ Fiber 7g
Low Fat Milk	110 calories /Protein 10g
Vanilla Low Fat Yogurt	½ cup/ 95 calories/ Protein 6g

Note: Increase fiber by adding fresh fruit, berries, small amounts of nuts or flaxseeds to hot cereals or whole grain pancakes. Avoid juices and eat the whole fruit instead.

Add non-flavored protein powder to hot cereals if you want to increase the protein without preparing eggs or a meat. Remember that you ideally want to get a minimum of 15 grams of protein with breakfast.

Protein/Fiber Lunch & Dinner Choices

Fresh or canned Salmon	2 oz/ 80 calories/ Protein 12g
Low Fat Burrito	6 oz/ 260 calories/ Protein 13g/ Fiber 7g
Cattle Drive Chicken Chile	1 cup/ 190 calories/ Protein 17g/ Fiber 1g

Progresso Beef Barley Soup	1 cup/ 110 calories/ Protein 8g/ Fiber 3g
Teriyaki Chicken Bowl	(354 g) 460 calories/ Protein 20g/ Fiber 3g
Cottage Cheese	(1/2 Cup) /Protein 14g
Chicken Breast (skinless)	4 oz/190 calories/ Protein 42g/ Fat calories 22
Lots of Veggies	About 3-4 grams of fiber per serving

Note: Add pinto, black, white or kidney beans to salads, soups and casseroles for an excellent source of fiber and additional protein. Add a wide variety of chopped veggies to soups and sauces as well for increased flavor and nutritional value.

Healthy Snack Choices

Balance Bar	1 bar/210 calories/ Protein 15g
Most Nuts	1 oz/ 160 calories/ Protein 6g/ Fiber 3g
Olives	(8) 50 calories
Whole Wheat crackers	(3) 110 calories/ Protein 2g/ Fiber 1g
Most fruits	100 to 150 calories per / Fiber 3g
Baby Carrots	3 oz/ 40 calories/ Fiber 3g

Eating with Danna in the Real World

People ask me all the time how I eat on a day to day basis. Well, how I eat may not be what you would enjoy. However, just for kicks, here's an example of how I ate the day after Thanksgiving. You'll note I ate just over 2,000 calories which I happen to know is exactly what I burned because I went for a 400 calorie walk. You can see how easy it is to eat that many calories without going overboard. You can also see that with some very minor modifications in my second example, how I can easily decrease that by 600 calories. I hope this example will help you realize how small choices make a big difference day after day...not just the day after Thanksgiving.

The "Day After" Thanksgiving - 2,030 calories

Breakfast
Egg Beaters with ½ ounce of cheddar cheese
1 Piece Orowheat toast, lightly buttered
Coffee with 1 tablespoon cream
400 calories / 14g protein / 4g fiber

Snack
Green Tea
Balance Bar
200 calories / 15g protein

Lunch
3 ounces turkey with ¼ cup Cranberry Sauce
3 ounces baby carrots
½ cup of stuffing (just because it tastes great)
½ cup green bean casserole
450 calories/ 18g protein / 6g fiber

Snack
1 ounce of almonds
Apple
260 calories / 6g protein / 6g fiber

Dinner
2 cups Turkey vegetable and noodle soup
1 sourdough roll
Green salad with Balsamic vinegar and olive oil
450 calories/ 25g protein / 6g fiber

Dessert
Decaf coffee with one tablespoon cream
½ piece Homemade apple/raspberry pie (left ½ of crust)
225 calories

Total Calories: 2030 • Protein: 78g • Fiber: 24g

Modified "Day After" Thanksgiving - 1,425 calories

Breakfast
½ cup Egg Beaters
1 Piece Oroweat toast, lightly buttered
½ banana
Coffee with cream
395 calories / 14g protein / 6g fiber

Snack
Green Tea
½ Balance Bar
100 calories / 7.5g protein

Lunch
3 ounces turkey with ¼ cup Cranberry Sauce
3 ounces baby carrots
½ cup green bean casserole
Sliced apple
450 calories/ 18g protein / 9g fiber

Snack
½ ounce of almonds
80 calories / 3g protein / 3g fiber

Dinner
2 cups Turkey vegetable and noodle soup
Green salad with Balsamic vinegar and olive oil
300 calories/ 25g protein / 6g fiber

Dessert
Decaf coffee with cream
2 Hershey's Kisses
100 calories

Total Calories: 1425 • Protein: 67.5g • Fiber: 24g
Resource: www.TheCalorieCounter.com

PERSONAL RELFLECTION

Answer the following questions on your own or with your group:

1. As you reviewed all the healthy eating and cooking ideas, what were the top three ideas you liked?

2. What are your greatest weaknesses in how you shop, eat or cook?

3. What will you do to improve in these areas?

4. Are you a procrastinator? Yes or no, now is a great time to take action. Begin to create your shopping list today. Keep adding to it over the next day and then schedule a time to go shopping when you are not in a hurry taking extra care to read labels and look for healthier food choices.

BUILD A STRONG SPIRITUAL FOUNDATION

Meditate on the following scripture and answer the corresponding questions:

"Search me, O God, and know my heart; try me and know my anxious thoughts; and see if there be any harmful way in me, and lead me in the everlasting way." —Psalm 139: 23-24

1. Of course, the psalmist knew that God knew his heart through and through. But, his desire was for God to reflect it back to him and to lead him down the right path. This is a great example of surrender. How can you surrender your struggles more fully to the Lord?

2. What are your anxious thoughts with respect to your body or lifestyle?

3. Since Jesus told us in Philippians 4:6 to be "anxious for nothing", how do we address this in our lives in a practical way?

4. Many people are living under great stress and anxiety which contributes to overeating and many health and relational issues. Spend time this week evaluating and praying about the stress and/or anxiety in your life.

NOURISH YOUR SPIRIT

Spiritual life-changing victory requires daily nourishment. Continue to nourish your spirit daily in four ways:

1. Pray as if it is the air you breathe.

This week, make it a practice to say a prayer before putting anything into your mouth. When you ask God to bless the food, also ask Him to convict you if you are making poor choices or eating too much.

2. Nourish your soul and spirit with God's Word daily.

Are you in the Word daily? If yes, GREAT! If not, take at least five minutes each day and nourish yourself with the most important nutrient available...His truth.

3. Digest its truths through meditation.

Meditate on our verse for this week and ask the Lord to reveal the areas of your heart and mind that need renewal. Let Him lead you in the everlasting way that brings great peace. Do a word search on the word "peace" in the New Testament and see what you learn about dealing with stress and anxiety.

4. Practice the presence of God.

How have you been doing with becoming aware of God's continual presence in your life? How is this impacting your life? Make it a lifetime commitment to grow in this exercise. For greater inspiration in this area, read the story of Brother Lawrence called *Practicing the Presence of God* or A. W. Tozer's book, *The Pursuit of God.*

PRAYER FOR WEEK SEVEN

Dear Lord, It is my desire to put the truths I learn from your Word and from this program into practice. Help me to have wisdom when I shop, cook and eat out. I pray that your Spirit will prompt me with a conviction of how each choice makes a difference and to bring to mind the ideas I have learned. I also ask that you help me to manage my time in a way that puts my health as a priority. Teach me and transform me in Your perfect timing. In Jesus name, Amen.

SUGGESTED READING – WEEK SEVEN

☐ Practicing the Presence of God

☐ The Pursuit of God

☐ Healthy Cookbooks!

B O N U S   S E C T I O N

RESOURCE: *LivingCookbook.com*

A wonderful computer program is available from www.livingcookbook.com. You can enter any recipe and it will kick out a complete nutrition label, compile a cookbook for you, shopping list and more. So if you're wondering the nutritional value of all those yummy family recipes, here's an easy way to find out. *You can download it for a free trial of 25 uses and/or purchase it for $30.00.*

Danna's Healthy Custard

    2 cups of 1 percent low fat milk

    3 lightly beaten eggs (or egg substitute equivalent)

    ¼ cup sugar

    ¼ teaspoon salt

    ½ teaspoon vanilla

Scald milk in a saucepan. Remove from heat and slowly stir in eggs. Then, stir salt, sugar and vanilla. Pour into 6 custard cups and sprinkle with nutmeg or cinnamon. Bake in a pan of hot water at 325 degrees for 30 to 40 minutes.

Caribbean Chicken

½ cup lemon juice	3 jalapeno peppers, seeded and chopped*
1/3 cup honey	3 tsp dried thyme
3 tablespoons canola oil	¾ teaspoon salt
6 green onions, sliced	¼ teaspoon ground allspice
¼ teaspoon ground nutmeg	

6 boneless skinless chicken breast halves (1-1/2 pounds)

Place the first nine ingredients (all but the chicken) in a blender or food processor; cover and process until smooth. Pour ½ cup into a small bowl for basting; cover and refrigerate. Pour remaining marinade into a large resealable plastic bag; add chicken. Seal bag and turn to coat; refrigerate for up to 6 hours.

Drain and discard marinade. Coat grill rack with nonstick cooking spray before starting the grill. Grill chicken, covered, over medium heat for 4-6 minutes on each side or until juices run clear, basting frequently with the reserved marinate. Yield: 6 servings.

Nutritional Analysis: One serving (1 chicken breast half) equals 205 calories, 6 g fat (1 g saturated fat), 66 mg cholesterol, 272 mg sodium, 11 g carbohydrate, trace fiber, 27 g protein. Diabetic Exchanges: 3 lean meat, ½ starch.

Coleslaw with Garden Veggies

1/4 cup reduced fat mayo	4 cups shredded cabbage
1/4 cup nonfat sour cream	1/2 cup grated carrot
1 Tbsp sugar	1/3 cup thinly sliced red bell pepper
2 Tbsp lemon juice	1/3 cup thinly sliced green bell pepper
3/4 tsp celery seeds	1/3 cup thinly sliced red onion
1/4 tsp salt	Raisins (optional)
1/8 tsp pepper	

In large bowl, mix together mayo, sour cream, sugar, lemon juice, celery seeds, salt and pepper. Add the remaining ingredients and toss to combine. Cover and refrigerate 3 hours. *Makes 6 servings. 74 calories, 10g carbohydrate, 3g fat, 2g protein.*

Potato and Bell Pepper Frittata

1 Tbsp olive oil

8 oz red potatoes, thinly sliced

1/2 cup sliced red onion

1/2 of a red bell pepper, thinly sliced

1/2 of a yellow bell pepper, thinly sliced

1/2 cup broccoli, chopped

2 tsp fresh chopped sage or dried rubbed sage

1 tsp salt

1/2 tsp freshly group pepper

8 eggs

2 cups plus 1/4 cup shredded Parmesan cheese

1. Preheat oven to 350. Heat olive oil in a 12-inch nonstick oven proof skillet over medium heat. Add potatoes, onion, bell peppers and broccoli; cover and cook, stirring occasionally, until vegetables are tender, 10 minutes. Stir in 1 teaspoon of the sage, 1/2 teaspoon of the salt, and 1/4 teaspoon of the pepper.

2. Whisk together the eggs, 2 cups of the cheese, and the remaining sage, salt and pepper; pour over vegetables in skillet and cook until edges of eggs just begin to set, 3 minutes.

3. Sprinkle top with the remaining cheese and bake until center is set, 8 minutes. Invert onto a serving plate. Makes 4 servings. *Nutritional Analysis: 435 calories, 27g fat, 33g protein, 14g carbohydrates.*

Salmon with Maple Syrup and Toasted Almonds

Six 6-ounce salmon fillets	3 Tbsp low-sodium soy sauce
Cooking spray	1 Tbsp Dijon mustard
1/4 cup packed brown sugar	1/4 tsp black pepper
1/4 cup maple syrup	4 tsp sliced almonds, toasted

Preheat oven to 425. Place fillets in a 13x9-inch baking dish coated with cooking spray. Combine sugar, syrup, soy sauce, mustard and black pepper; pour sugar mixture over fillets. Cover with foil; bake at 425 for 10 minutes. Remove foil; sprinkle the fillets with almonds. Bake an additional 10 minutes or until fish flakes easily when tested with a fork. Serve with sugar mixture. Yield 6 servings.

Nutritional Analysis: 373 calories, 12.78g total fat, 2.56 sat fat, 418mg sodium, 799mg potassium, 43g protein.

Couscous, Black Bean & Feta Salad

1 can (15 oz) black beans, rinsed and drained	1/2 cup chopped celery
1 1/2 cups chopped tomatoes	1/2 cup chopped green onions
1 1/2 cups (or 1 box) plain couscous, cooked	1/2 cup fat-free Italian dressing
1 pkg (4 oz) crumbled feta cheese	
2 Tbsp chopped fresh cilantro or parsley	

Mix all ingredients and refrigerate. Makes 5 servings. *Nutritional Analysis: 222 calories, 5.6g total fat, 3.56 sat fat, 683mg sodium, 468mg potassium, 7.45g fiber, 4.65g sugar, 12g protein.*

Seven-Vegetable Salad

A beautiful, crisp and flavorful salad

1 cup cut fresh green beans

1 cup fresh sugar snap peas

1 cup sliced yellow summer squash

1 cup sliced zucchini

1/2 cup julienne onion

4 tsp minced chives

2 small tomatoes, seeded and
chopped

1 cup coarsely grated carrots

2/3 cup lowfat Italian salad
dressing

2 tsp dried basil

In a saucepan, bring 2 in. of water to a boil. Add beans, peas, yellow squash, zucchini and onion. Reduce heat; cover and simmer for 2-3 minutes or until vegetables are crisp-tender. Drain; rinse with cold water and pat dry. Place vegetables in a bowl; add the remaining ingredients. Gently stir to coat. Refrigerate until serving. Yield: 12 servings. *Nutritional Analysis: 1/2 cup equals 47 calories, 2g fat, 132mg sodium, 6g carbohydrate, 2g fiber, 1g protein.*

Chicken Parmigiano

1/2 cup dry bread crumbs

3 Tbsp grated Parmesan cheese

3/4 tsp Italian seasoning

1/2 tsp garlic powder

3/4 cup shredded part-skim mozzarella

1/2 tsp salt

1/4 cup egg substitute

4 boneless skinless chicken
breast halves

1 jar (26 oz) meatless spaghetti
sauce

1/4 cup shredded parmesan

In a shallow bowl, combine the bread crumbs, grated Parmesan, Italian seasoning, garlic powder and salt. In another bowl, beat egg substitute. Dip chicken in egg substitute, then roll in crumbs. Place in a 13x9x2-inch baking dish coated with nonstick cooking spray. Bake uncovered, at 375 for 10 minutes. Turn chicken; bake for 10 minutes. Pour spaghetti sauce over chicken; bake for 5 minutes. Sprinkle with cheeses; bake 10 minutes longer or until chicken juices run clear. Yield: 4 servings. *Nutritional Analysis: 412 calories, 15g fat (5g saturated), 88mg cholesterol, 1,420mg sodium, 32g carbohydrate, 5g fiber, 37g protein.*

Vegetable Quiche Cups to Go

¾ cup to 1 cup Egg Substitute (depends on the brand you buy)

¾ cup shredded reduced-fat cheese

¼ cup diced onion

¼ cup diced green pepper

¼ cup diced celery

1 pkg. frozen chopped spinach

Salt, pepper, and hot sauce (3 –6 drops) to taste.

Foil cup cake liners (12)

Preheat oven to 350 degrees. Place foil cup cake liners in muffin pan. Spray Pam spray into the cup cake liners. Microwave the frozen spinach for 2 ½ minutes on high. Squeeze all the excess liquid from the spinach. In a mixing bowl combine spinach, onion, celery, egg substitute, cheese, salt and pepper to taste. Add hot sauce if desired. Mix well. Spoon mixture evenly into the 12 cup cake liners. Bake in the oven about 20 minutes or until knife comes out clean. Can be frozen and reheated in the microwave (without foil liners). A good breakfast or lunch alternative.

Nutritional Analysis: 2 quiches: 77 calories,   9g protein, 3g carbohydrate, 2g fiber.

WEEK 8

The Click Factor

In This Section:

- The "Click Factor"
- Writing Your Own Powerful Self Talk
- Logging for Success

What's a "Click Factor"?

Teaching people how to make lasting lifestyle changes can be a frustrating venture. No matter how much knowledge you give, how many great ideas you provide or how inspiring your enthusiasm or personal testimony, you have no control over what the recipients will ultimately do. In truth, I have finally resolved that my job is to impart truth. In the end, I must leave the results up to you and God.

In the revised edition of *Scale Down,* I added some teaching on the subject of what I've come to call the "click factor". The click factor is the experience, attitude or perspective that will motivate you sufficiently and sustain you indefinitely in your quest for a leaner and healthier body. If you find it...you've mostly likely discovered *your key* to permanent victory. I think that this concept is important enough to repeat in this study guide. I encourage you to review the concept and then actually go on a journey to discover your key (if you have not already).

I get email from all over the country as both men and women are actually "clicking" as they read *Scale Down* and begin implementing the principles. When I get the opportunity to speak personally with someone, I always want to know what "clicked" for them. I have two examples that I hope will inspire you to find your "Click Factor".

Small steps add up

When *Scale Down* was first released in the March 2003, I had the privilege of being interviewed on one of the most popular and largest Christian radio talk shows in the country, *Midday Connection*. The host, Anita Lustrea works for Moody Broadcasting and was a wonderfully enthusiastic host. She was excited about the principles I taught, asked great questions and juggled an hour's worth of calls from her listeners as I answered questions on every aspect of lifestyle change. The really cool thing was that six months later, when she asked me back for another interview she revealed *on air* that she had lost 35 pounds since reading Scale Down. Now, almost three years later, she has lost a total of 50 pounds and kept it off. When asked what "clicked" for her, Anita said that she finally realized that *little things really did add up* when she practiced them *consistently*. As she started eating more protein and fiber, her energy increased and she began to move more. One day at a time, each little change slowly brought more visible rewards and she thought, *"I can do this for a lifetime!"*

Worn out tapes

In late 2004, I received a call from a client who had taken my 8-week program about three years ago. In her message she said that she had lost one hundred pounds and had completely worn out her self-talk CD and needed a new one for continued encouragement. For Kathleen, the "Click Factor" was learning the power of transforming her mind with healthy thinking about food and her body. Even more exciting was the fact that she did not even know Christ as her Savior when she first took the program…but she does now! As of this writing,

Kathleen has become an important part of our *Scale Down* team and is helping us facilitate classes in San Diego.

In addition to using our self-talk CD, Kathleen did a great job identifying her lies and writing new positive self-talk very specific to her life. She also found great benefit in recording some of her own messages in her own voice. That is why I asked her to contribute to this week's study, by sharing how she did this. I have a very strong sense that this is probably the single most important "Click Factor" for most people. That is, reprogramming your self-talk.

Trigger Talk...Just DO it!

After you go through the exercise below individually or with your group, please do yourself a *HUGE* favor and begin practicing your "trigger talk" as discussed in the *"You Are What You Think"* session. The time you take to write or record new messages will be without value if you don't consistently tell yourself those truths day after day, week after week, month after month. If you want to experience victory like Anita and Kathleen, take some consistent small steps and speak truth daily into your own mind. Then, call me so I can celebrate with you!

Writing your own self-talk - Kathleen's Tips

Kathleen defines healthy self-talk in this way: *"Statements of truth that I want to believe, said as if I already believe them."* As you've already learned, *healthy* self-talk is first and foremost about telling yourself truth. But, it's not truth as you are living it, but rather truth of the potential and possibility of what you can do and be *if and when* you surrender to God's principles and purpose for your life. Here are some Kathleen's suggestions for writing your own healthy, truth-based self-talk:

Guidelines to writing your own self-talk

1. Keep it positive. Avoid using negative words like *no, never* or *can't.*

2. Keep it in the present. Avoid using words like *will, should* or *"going to".* Rather use phrases like *"I am"* or *"I have".*

3. Make it memorable. Unless you are recording a self-talk cassette to listen to, keep your statements simple and easy to recall/repeat (especially in times of temptation). For recordings, studies have shown people actually learn faster when studying while listening to baroque music. Try playing Mozart or Beethoven in the background.

4. Remember the most dominant thought wins. You will believe what you tell yourself most often, so personalize a few self-talk messages and make them part of your daily life. Be sure to include the self-talk to balance all three areas of your life: physical, mental and spiritual.

5. Go back to your four evaluations and notice how most are worded positively. Circle the ones you rated lowest and use some of those statements for your personal self-talk.

6. Find two or three scripture that speak directly to your personal challenges. Memorize them and use them when you feel tempted, defeated or low.

Positive Self-Talk Examples

Instead of:	*Change to:*
I will not eat junk food.	I choose to eat healthy food and love it.
I should take better care of myself.	I deserve good health and take good care of myself.
I will lose 20 pounds.	I am eating and exercising for maximum health.

Self-Talk Examples for Each Dimension

Physical

I enjoy exercise and love the way it makes me feel!

Mental

I am a strong and Christ-confident with a positive life and perspective.

Spiritual

I am an obedient and faithful child of God. I know I can do all things through Christ who strengthens me.

Write some of your own:

_____

_____

_____

_____

PERSONAL REFLECTION

Answer the following questions on your own or with your group:

1. How are you doing?

Now that you have been on your journey for a while, it is time to revisit how you are "balancing the dimensions of your life". On a scale from 1-10 (with 10 being the best), how do you rate yourself in the following areas:

- Your physical health and wellness _____

- Your thoughts, life perspective, attitudes about life _____

- Your emotions, feelings about yourself or others _____

- Your behavior such as habits, lifestyle, work and stress _____

- Your spiritual dimension, time with God, life purpose _____

2. What's your ONE THING?

Once again, what is the "one thing" in each area that will make the biggest difference in experiencing victory in that dimension? Pray for wisdom to know what that is and the appropriate and "God-honoring" action to take. Then write it down next to each area below:

- Your physical health and wellness "ONE THING":

- _____

- Your thoughts, life perspective, attitudes about life "ONE THING":

- _____

- Your emotions, feelings about yourself or others "ONE THING":

- _____

- Your behavior such as habits, lifestyle, work and stress "ONE THING":

- _____

- Your spiritual dimension, time with God, life purpose "ONE THING":

- _____

3. Take Action... Paper, prayer and practice!

Now, spend some time this week deciding how you are going to weave these actions into your life. This is a very important exercise that should take considerable prayer, reflection and planning.

BUILD A STRONG SPIRITUAL FOUNDATION

Meditate on this scripture and answer the corresponding questions:

And, He said to him, "You shall love the Lord Your God with all your heart, and with all your soul and with all your mind.
—Matthew 22:37

1. How do you develop an all-consuming love for God?

2. How does that kind of love change your life?

3. What can you do every day to deepen your love for God?

4. What is stopping you from doing that everyday?

5. What will you do specifically this week to make your relationship with God the most important single thing in your life?

NOURISH YOUR SPIRIT

Spiritual life-changing victory requires daily nourishment. Nourish your spirit daily in four ways:

1. Pray as if it is the air you breathe.

Matthew 22:37 is the core of all things important. When we experience this kind of love for God, our thoughts, feelings and behaviors will follow. Pray daily that God will impart the ability to love Him first and foremost.

2. *Nourish your soul and spirit with God's Word daily.*

To know and love God, we must know and love His Word since that is how He communicates with us. Remind yourself that His love letter is waiting to be read and reread so you will discover and experience the depth and breadth of His love which is beyond comprehension.

3. *Digest its truths through meditation.*

Memorize our verse this week and use it in your "trigger time" for the next several weeks. This will help you make the next step (practicing the presence of God) a daily reality in your life.

4. *Practice the presence of God.*

Go back through the last seven week's studies and list all the ideas for practicing God's presence. Write down two or three which are most helpful to you and DO THEM! He is here with you right now...and will be forever. Wouldn't it be incredible if that reality was always in the forefront of our thoughts?

PRAYER FOR WEEK EIGHT

Heavenly Father, thank you for the journey we have been on together. I know it has only just begun and I need your strength and guidance to stay on the path of healthy thinking and living. Please empower me with Your Spirit and give me the wisdom and self-discipline that comes only from You to stay the course. I praise you that You have made all things new and that I will someday know ultimate perfection. I love you, Lord. Amen.

Optional Section

Logging for Success

In This Section:

- Why take time to log?
- The *Scale Down* Daily Success Plan

Why Take Time to Log?

Statistics show that people who log their progress daily are the most successful. Take a few minutes each day to record your food choices, activity and workouts. Seeing your own triumphs in writing will inspire and motivate you. It's documented proof of all your hard work!

The Scale Down Daily Success Plan

I have included a copy of the Scale Down Daily Success Plan. It is also available as a *free download on my website at dannademetre.com*. The log will give you tremendous insight into your own habits. We all say, "I should eat less," but do you really know how much you're eating now? We all say, "I should exercise more," but do you have any idea how many calories you're currently burning each day? Your log will help you pinpoint exactly where your problem areas are and help you set concrete, achievable goals.

To help you get a realistic picture of exactly what you're eating and how much you're moving, you may want to keep a daily log as you go through the program. Whether you're eating too much fat, eating too many calories, skimping on fiber, or neglecting exercise, your log will help you see a snapshot of your habits and help you hold yourself accountable to new behaviors.

Focus on the changes in your habits, not what the scale says or the size of your muscles. Your body will always respond to *consistent* action. As I've said before, do the right things long enough and your best body will follow!

S C A L E   D O W N   D A I L Y   S U C C E S S   P L A N

My NUTRITION GOALS for Today:		*Cals*	*Carbo*	*Pro*	*Fat*	*Fiber*	MultiVitamins ❑ 1st ❑ 2nd		
						30 grams	Antioxidant ❑ Yes ❑ No		
MEALS	FOOD ITEMS	Cals	Carbo	Pro	Fat	Fiber	Hunger Before (Rate 1-5)	Hunger After (Rate 1-5)	WATER
Breakfast									❑
									❑
SNACK									❑
Lunch									❑
									❑
									❑
SNACK									❑
Dinner									❑
									❑
									❑
									❑
SNACK									❑
TOTALS	# Fruits _____ # Vegies _____								

ACTIVITIES – Describe what you did today in these lifestyle areas

SPIRITUAL	
MENTAL	Listened to SELF TALK: ❑ ❑ / ❑ ❑
PHYSICAL	❑ AEROBIC How long? ❑ MUSCLE WORK Describe: ❑ STRETCHING
ENERGY	❑ Great! ❑ Good ❑ Fair ❑ Poor
SLEEP	# of hours lastnight: _____ Rested today: ❑ Yes ❑ No

ACTIVITY LOG	Cals IN	Cals OUT	Total Steps or Miles	NET	Cumulative (+ -)

What went well? _____

Ways to improve tomorrow: _____

Daily Success Plan By Danna Demetre | Free Download On www.DannaDemetre.com

Start a Small Group and Get a Free Leader's Guide!

A step by step guide to leading a Scale Down class, this guide correlates with the Scale Down book, workbook and six-week video series. It includes recommendations for meeting format, recommended resources, topical insights and facilitator tips for each week. All you need to do is gather and support your participants and let Danna do the teaching via the DVDs! The Scale Down program has been used in churches and homes across America – helping people discover lasting victory over unhealthy habits of body and mind.

Start your own small group in your home or at your church and receive a free Leader's Guide valued at $10. Simply order the Scale Down DVD set to qualify for this free offer.